POETRY
FOR THE GRAMMAR STAGE
Student Guide

Laura Bateman and Dayna Grant

MEMORIA PRESS

MEMORIA PRESS
www.MemoriaPress.com

POETRY FOR THE GRAMMAR STAGE

STUDENT GUIDE
Laura Bateman and Dayna Grant

ISBN 978-1-5477-0001-1

Third Edition © 2018 Memoria Press | 1119

Cover illustration by John William Waterhouse

CONTENTS

How to Teach a Poem
A Lesson to an Enriching Poem Analysis
David M. Wright

Note: These steps work equally well in a homeschool situation or in a classroom. The parenthetical "(or child)" below signals for a homeschool environment.

1. **Teach the poem from your *heart*.**
   - Select a poem that *moves* you; or at least try to summon an appreciation for the poem you are about to teach. Open yourself up to the artistic experience of the poem. If the poem speaks to you, you can discuss it effectively with your students (or child).

2. **Read the poem aloud while your students (or child) follow along in their books.**
   - The teacher or parent should read it aloud here — to demonstrate a proper reading with sound, rhythm, emphasis, enunciation, etc.

3. **Call on a *particular student* (or your child) to read the poem aloud. This will now be the *second* reading. The other students should continue to follow along in their books.**
   - Note: If using this in a classroom, use your discretion here with regard to the student you choose to call upon to read. For example, you may want to ask a student who is usually hesitant to say much in class.

4. **Call on a *different* student (or your child) to *paraphrase* the poem — that is, to provide a summary of the lines and stanzas in his or her own words. Either of these options is good:**
   - One student can paraphrase, stanza by stanza, the whole poem.
   - Several students can be involved by having a different student paraphrase each stanza.

5. **Ask a *different* student (or your child), "What stands out to you in the poem?"**
   - This question initiates meaningful thought and discussion. It allows the students (or child) to *observe*, to *notice*, and to *like* various elements in the poem.
   - Ask three or four more students the same question. Use this to generate good class discussion.

6. **In the literature and poetry guides in the upper school years, students will be required to identify the Central One Idea of each work studied. The comprehension questions and analytical exercises in this guide will help prepare students for this more advanced work. Lead students with questions that help them consider important poetic elements such as *the title, the speaker, diction, figures of speech, tone and attitude, symbol, imagery, irony, shifts/changes*, etc. (If you need help in understanding these poetic elements, refer to the Glossary in the Appendix, or acquire a copy of M. H. Abrams' *A Glossary of Literary Terms*.)**
   - Some of these will have already been discussed in Step 5, and now you will add others that you deem important but have yet to be discussed.
   - As the teacher or parent, state your version of the Central One Idea with supporting points (the elements and features in the poem that convey the Central One Idea).

7. **Discuss the *title*.**

    • Teachers and students often forget to consider the title in their analysis. Yet the title usually does embody the Central One Idea, so it is essential to reflect upon it. It should be noted that sometimes the title speaks only to the *subject* of the poem, or perhaps the title is just the first line. In either case, ask, "What title would you give this poem?" Or, "Which line would you pull out to serve as the best title?"

8. **If more time is warranted or needed, lead a further general discussion and reflection on the poem.**

    • You may include here a discussion of elements in the poem that have yet to be discussed or other sub-ideas and themes that have yet to be mentioned. Or perhaps discuss the poet and/ or the time period and culture in which the poem is situated.

9. **Call on a different student (or your child) to *summarize* in her own words what she now knows about the poem.**

Teaching Guidelines

Teachers should familiarize themselves with the concepts and terms covered in the Appendix before starting this study guide with students. Concepts that are referred to frequently in the "Analyze" and "Comprehension Questions" sections are explained there with examples. The Glossary is also a good reference for students as they complete the study guide.

THE PLEIADES
Amy Lowell

By day you cannot see the sky
For it is up so very high.
You look and look, but it's so blue
That you can never see right through.

But when night comes it is quite plain,
And all the stars are there again.
They seem just like old friends to me,
I've known them all my life you see.

There is the dipper first, and there
Is Cassiopeia in her chair,
Orion's Belt, the Milky Way,
And lots I know but cannot say.

One group looks like a swarm of bees,
Papa says they're the Pleiades;
But I think they must be the toy
Of some nice little angel boy.

Perhaps his jackstones which today
He has forgot to put away,
And left them lying on the sky
Where he will find them by and by.

I wish he'd come and play with me.
We'd have such fun, for it would be
A most unusual thing for boys
To feel that they had stars for toys!

COPYBOOK: Copy the poem in the space below. Use the box on the previous page to illustrate the poem.

VOCABULARY:

Cassiopeia	a constellation named for Queen Cassiopeia from Greek mythology
Orion's Belt	the three brightest stars in the constellation Orion
Milky Way	the galaxy containing our solar system
Pleiades	a group of stars that are part of the constellation Taurus
jackstones	metal pieces used in playing the game of jacks

ANALYZE:

1. Think about the rhyming structure of this poem. Label each line and then write out the rhyme scheme.

   _____

2. Who is the speaker of the poem? _____

1	By day you cannot see the sky	_____
2	For it is up so very high.	_____
3	You look and look, but it's so blue	_____
4	That you can never see right through.	_____
5	But when night comes it is quite plain,	_____
6	And all the stars are there again.	_____
7	They seem just like old friends to me,	_____
8	I've known them all my life you see.	_____
9	There is the dipper first, and there	_____
10	Is Cassiopeia in her chair,	_____
11	Orion's Belt, the Milky Way,	_____
12	And lots I know but cannot say.	_____

13	One group looks like a swarm of bees,	_____
14	Papa says they're the Pleiades;	_____
15	But I think they must be the toy	_____
16	Of some nice little angel boy.	_____
17	Perhaps his jackstones which today	_____
18	He has forgot to put away,	_____
19	And left them lying on the sky	_____
20	Where he will find them by and by.	_____
21	I wish he'd come and play with me.	_____
22	We'd have such fun, for it would be	_____
23	A most unusual thing for boys	_____
24	To feel that they had stars for toys!	_____

COMPREHENSION QUESTIONS:

1. How are stars like old friends? _____
   _____
   _____
   _____

2. What is "the dipper"? _____
   _____
   _____
   _____

3. Discuss each constellation mentioned._____
   _____
   _____
   _____
   _____
   _____
   _____
   _____

4. What is the imagery used to describe the Pleiades?_____
   _____
   _____
   _____

5. What story does the author create to explain the stars? _____
   _____
   _____
   _____

THE HAPPY FARMER
Unknown

Let the mighty and great
Roll in splendor and state,
I envy them not, I declare it.
I eat my own lamb,
My own chicken and ham;
I shear my own sheep and I wear it.

I have lawns and green bowers,
Fresh fruits and fine flowers,
The lark is my bright morning charmer.
So God bless the plow
In the future as now—
A health and long life to the farmer.

COPYBOOK: Copy the poem in the space below. Use the box on the previous page to illustrate the poem.

VOCABULARY:

splendor	great fame; glory
state	ceremony; pomp
shear	to remove fleece by cutting
bower	a shady, leafy spot

ANALYZE:

1. Think about the rhyming structure of this poem. Label each line and then write out the rhyme scheme.

   _____

2. Underline the places where this poem uses alliteration.

1 Let the mighty and great _____   7 I have lawns and green bowers, _____

2 Roll in splendor and state, _____   8 Fresh fruits and fine flowers, _____

3 I envy them not, I declare it. _____   9 The lark is my bright morning charmer. _____

4 I eat my own lamb, _____   10 So God bless the plow _____

5 My own chicken and ham; _____   11 In the future as now— _____

6 I shear my own sheep and I wear it. _____   12 A health and long life to the farmer. _____

COMPREHENSION QUESTIONS:

1. Who are the mighty and great? _____

_____

_____

_____

2. What does it mean to "roll in splendor and state"? Who do you think does this? _____

_____

_____

_____

3. Why does the farmer not envy the "mighty and great"? _____

_____

_____

_____

4. The farmer is able to sustain himself from his farm with almost everything he needs. What are the things

he is able to get from his farm? _____

_____

_____

_____

5. Why is the lark "a bright morning charmer"? _____

_____

_____

_____

6. The farmer asks God to "bless the plow." What does a plow represent to a farmer? _____

_____

_____

_____

7. The title of the poem reveals to us that this farmer is happy. Why is the farmer happy? _____

_____

_____

_____

THE HAYLOFT
Robert Louis Stevenson

Through all the pleasant meadow-side
The grass grew shoulder-high,
Till the shining scythes went far and wide
And cut it down to dry.

These green and sweetly smelling crops
They led in wagons home;
And they piled them here in mountain tops
For mountaineers to roam.

Here is Mount Clear, Mount Rusty-Nail,
Mount Eagle and Mount High;—
The mice that in these mountains dwell,
No happier are than I!

O what a joy to clamber there,
O what a place for play,
With the sweet, the dim, the dusty air,
The happy hills of hay!

COPYBOOK: Copy the poem in the space below. Use the box on the previous page to illustrate the poem.

VOCABULARY:

scythe	a tool with a long curved blade used for mowing or reaping
mountaineer	one who climbs mountains for sport
clamber	to climb with difficulty

ANALYZE:

1. Think about the rhyming structure of this poem. Label each line and then write out the rhyme scheme.

   _____

2. Who is the speaker of the poem? _____

   _____

3. Underline the places where this poem uses alliteration.

1 Through all the pleasant meadow-side   _____

2 The grass grew shoulder-high,   _____

3 Till the shining scythes went far and wide _____

4 And cut it down to dry.   _____

5 These green and sweetly smelling crops   _____

6 They led in wagons home;   _____

7 And they piled them here in mountain tops _____

8 For mountaineers to roam.   _____

9 Here is Mount Clear, Mount Rusty-Nail,   _____

10 Mount Eagle and Mount High;—   _____

11 The mice that in these mountains dwell,   _____

12 No happier are than I!   _____

13 O what a joy to clamber there,   _____

14 O what a place for play,   _____

15 With the sweet, the dim, the dusty air,   _____

16 The happy hills of hay!   _____

COMPREHENSION QUESTIONS:

1. Summarize the story of the poem in your own words. _____

   _____

   _____

   _____

2. Line 7 says "And they piled them here in mountain tops." Where is the hay piled? How do you know?

   _____

   _____

   _____

3. Who are the "mountaineers" roaming the mountains? How do you think they named the mountains?

   _____

   _____

   _____

   _____

   _____

TRY, TRY AGAIN
William Hickson

'Tis a lesson you should heed,
Try, try again;
If at first you don't succeed,
Try, try again;
Then your courage should appear,
For if you will persevere,
You will conquer, never fear,
Try, try again.

Once or twice though you should fail,
Try, try again;
If you would at last prevail,
Try, try again;

If we strive, 'tis no disgrace
Though we do not win the race;
What should you do in the case?
Try, try again.

If you find your task is hard,
Try, try again;
Time will bring you your reward,
Try, try again;
All that other folks can do,
Why, with patience, should not you?
Only keep this rule in view;
Try, try again.

COPYBOOK: Copy the poem in the space below. Use the box on the previous page to illustrate the poem.

VOCABULARY:

heed	to pay attention to
persevere	to remain constant to a purpose
prevail	to triumph; to succeed
strive	to exert much effort or energy; to try hard
disgrace	the loss of honor or reputation; shame

ANALYZE:

1. What is the refrain of this poem? _____

2. Think about the rhyming structure of this poem. Label each line and then write out the rhyme scheme.

   _____

3. Underline each occurrence of the word *if*.

1   'Tis a lesson you should heed,   _____

2   Try, try again;   _____

3   If at first you don't succeed,   _____

4   Try, try again;   _____

5   Then your courage should appear,   _____

6   For if you will persevere,   _____

7   You will conquer, never fear,   _____

8   Try, try again.   _____

9   Once or twice though you should fail,   _____

10   Try, try again;   _____

11   If you would at last prevail,   _____

12   Try, try again;   _____

13   If we strive, 'tis no disgrace   _____

14   Though we do not win the race;   _____

15   What should you do in the case?   _____

16   Try, try again.   _____

17   If you find your task is hard,   _____

18   Try, try again;   _____

19   Time will bring you your reward,   _____

20   Try, try again;   _____

21   All that other folks can do,   _____

22   Why, with patience, should not you?   _____

23   Only keep this rule in view;   _____

24   Try, try again.   _____

COMPREHENSION QUESTIONS:

1. Why does the author repeat the line "try, try again"? _____

    _____

    _____

    _____

2. What does the author seem to be emphasizing with the repetition of the word *if*? _____

    _____

    _____

    _____

3. What are the reasons the poem gives to keep trying? _____

    _____

    _____

    _____

4. In the second stanza, to what does "win the race" refer? Why is it not a disgrace when we don't win?

    _____

    _____

    _____

5. More often than not, success is waiting for you if you keep trying. What are some areas in which you are

    tempted to give up quickly? _____

    _____

    _____

    _____

    _____

    _____

    _____

    _____

THE SPIDER AND THE FLY
Mary Howitt

"Will you walk into my parlour?" said the Spider to
    the Fly,
"'Tis the prettiest little parlour that ever you did spy;
The way into my parlour is up a winding stair,
And I've a many curious things to shew when you
    are there."
"Oh no, no," said the little Fly, "to ask me is in vain,
For who goes up your winding stair can ne'er come
    down again."

"I'm sure you must be weary, dear, with soaring up
    so high;
Will you rest upon my little bed?" said the Spider to
    the Fly.
"There are pretty curtains drawn around; the sheets
    are fine and thin,
And if you like to rest awhile, I'll snugly tuck you in!"
"Oh no, no," said the little Fly, "for I've often heard it
    said,
They never, never wake again, who sleep upon
    your bed!"

Said the cunning Spider to the Fly, "Dear friend
what can I do,
To prove the warm affection I've always felt for you?
I have within my pantry, good store of all that's nice;
I'm sure you're very welcome—will you please to
    take a slice?"
"Oh no, no," said the little Fly, "kind Sir, that cannot be,
I've heard what's in your pantry, and I do not wish
    to see!"

"Sweet creature!" said the Spider, "you're witty and
    you're wise,
How handsome are your gauzy wings, how brilliant
    are your eyes!
I've a little looking-glass upon my parlour shelf,
If you'll step in one moment, dear, you shall
    behold yourself."
"I thank you, gentle sir," she said, "for what you're
    pleased to say,
And bidding you good morning now, I'll call
another day."

The Spider turned him round about, and went into
    his den,
For well he knew the silly Fly would soon come
    back again:
So he wove a subtle web, in a little corner sly,
And set his table ready, to dine upon the Fly.
Then he came out to his door again, and merrily
    did sing,
"Come hither, hither, pretty Fly, with the pearl and
    silver wing;
Your robes are green and purple—there's a crest
upon your head;
Your eyes are like the diamond bright, but mine are
    dull as lead!"

Alas, alas! how very soon this silly little Fly,
Hearing his wily, flattering words, came slowly
    flitting by;
With buzzing wings she hung aloft, then near and
    nearer drew,
Thinking only of her brilliant eyes, and green and
    purple hue—
Thinking only of her crested head—poor foolish
    thing! At last,
Up jumped the cunning Spider, and fiercely held
    her fast.
He dragged her up his winding stair, into his
    dismal den,
Within his little parlour—but she ne'er came out again!

And now, dear little children, who may this story read,
To idle, silly, flattering words, I pray you ne'er give heed:
Unto an evil counsellor, close heart and ear and eye,
And take a lesson from this tale, of the Spider and
    the Fly.

COPYBOOK: Copy select parts of the poem in the space below. Use the box on the next page to illustrate the poem.

_____

_____

_____

_____

_____

_____

_____

_____

_____

_____

_____

_____

_____

_____

_____

_____

_____

_____

_____

_____

_____

_____

_____

_____

_____

_____

_____

VOCABULARY:

cunning   skillfully deceitful; subtle

gauzy   transparent; thin; light

subtle   almost unnoticeable

wily   crafty; sly; tricky

flattering   falsely complimenting; excessively praising

ANALYZE:

1. Think about the rhyming structure of this poem. Write out the rhyme scheme. _____

_____

COMPREHENSION QUESTIONS:

1. In what ways does the Spider try to get the Fly to come into the house? _____

   _____

   _____

   _____

   _____

2. Which of these techniques is successful? Why does the Fly return? _____

   _____

   _____

   _____

   _____

3. Why is the parlour described as the "prettiest parlour" early in the poem, but as having a "dismal den"

   inside it later in the poem? _____

   _____

   _____

   _____

   _____

4. What is the message the speaker is giving at the end of the poem? _____

   _____

   _____

   _____

   _____

OUR HOUSE
Dorothy Brown Thompson

Our house is small—
The lawn and all
Can scarcely hold the flowers,
Yet every bit,
The whole of it,
Is precious, for it's ours!

From door to door,
From roof to floor,
From wall to wall we love it;

We wouldn't change
For something strange
One shabby corner of it!

The space complete
In cubic feet
From cellar floor to rafter
Just measures right,
And not too tight,
For us, and friends, and laughter!

COPYBOOK: Copy the poem in the space below. Use the box on the previous page to illustrate the poem.

_____

_____

_____

_____

_____

_____

_____

_____

_____

_____

_____

_____

_____

_____

_____

_____

_____

_____

_____

_____

_____

_____

_____

Dorothy Brown Thompson

VOCABULARY:

precious   valuable; beloved; something of special importance to the owner

shabby   showing signs of wear

rafter   a wooden beam near the ceiling that supports the roof

ANALYZE:

1. Think about the rhyming structure of this poem. Write out the rhyme scheme. _____

    _____

1	Our house is small—	_____	
2	The lawn and all	_____	
3	Can scarcely hold the flowers,	_____	
4	Yet every bit,	_____	
5	The whole of it,	_____	
6	Is precious, for it's ours!	_____	

7	From door to door,	_____
8	From roof to floor,	_____
9	From wall to wall we love it;	_____

10	We wouldn't change	_____
11	For something strange	_____
12	One shabby corner of it!	_____

13	The space complete	_____
14	In cubic feet	_____
15	From cellar floor to rafter	_____
16	Just measures right,	_____
17	And not too tight,	_____
18	For us, and friends, and laughter!	_____

COMPREHENSION QUESTIONS:

1. What might this house look like to an outsider who does not love it as much as the speaker of the poem?

   _____

   _____

   _____

   _____

2. Why does the speaker love the house so much, even though it seems to not be very large or pretty?

   _____

   _____

   _____

   _____

3. With what does the speaker fill the house? _____

   _____

   _____

   _____

4. What sort of house do you live in? What makes it "home" to you? _____

   _____

   _____

   _____

   _____

THE WIND
Robert Louis Stevenson

I saw you toss the kites on high
And blow the birds about the sky;
And all around I heard you pass,
Like ladies' skirts across the grass—
　　O wind, a-blowing all day long,
　　O wind, that sings so loud a song!

I saw the different things you did,
But always you yourself you hid.
I felt you push, I heard you call,

I could not see yourself at all—
　　O wind, a-blowing all day long,
　　O wind, that sings so loud a song!

O you that are so strong and cold,
O blower, are you young or old?
Are you a beast of field and tree,
Or just a stronger child than me?
　　O wind, a-blowing all day long,
　　O wind, that sings so loud a song!

COPYBOOK: Copy the poem in the space below. Use the box on the previous page to illustrate the poem.

VOCABULARY:

a-blowing: gusting; moving; releasing a loud breath

beast: an animal or other type of living creature

ANALYZE:

1. Think about the rhyming pattern of this poem. Label each line and then write out the rhyme scheme.

_____

_____

2. Underline instances of personification in this poem.

1   I saw you toss the kites on high   _____

2   And blow the birds about the sky;   _____

3   And all around I heard you pass,   _____

4   Like ladies' skirts across the grass—   _____

5   O wind, a-blowing all day long,   _____

6   O wind, that sings so loud a song!   _____

7   I saw the different things you did,   _____

8   But always you yourself you hid.   _____

9   I felt you push, I heard you call,   _____

10   I could not see yourself at all—   _____

11   O wind, a-blowing all day long,   _____

12   O wind, that sings so loud a song!   _____

13   O you that are so strong and cold,   _____

14   O blower, are you young or old?   _____

15   Are you a beast of field and tree,   _____

16   Or just a stronger child than me?   _____

17   O wind, a-blowing all day long,   _____

18   O wind, that sings so loud a song!   _____

COMPREHENSION QUESTIONS:

1. What is the purpose of using the poetic device of personification in this poem? _____

_____

_____

_____

2. Whom is the speaker addressing throughout this poem, and how do you know?_____

_____

_____

_____

3. How does the poet experience the wind, and in what way does he recognize that he cannot experience

the wind? _____

_____

_____

_____

4. What is one thing that the wind does that seems to frustrate the speaker to some degree? Why do you

think the poet included this? _____

_____

_____

_____

5. What two questions does the speaker ask the wind and what do these two questions reveal about what

the speaker wants to know about the wind?_____

_____

_____

_____

6. What effect does the repetition of the last two lines of each stanza have on the meaning and tone of

the poem? _____

_____

_____

UNTITLED
Johann Wolfgang von Goethe

We must not hope to be mowers,
And to gather the ripe old ears,
Unless we have first been sowers
And watered the furrows with tears.

It is not just as we take it,
This mystical world of ours,
Life's field will yield as we make it,
A harvest of thorns or of flowers.

COPYBOOK: Copy the poem in the space below. Use the box on the previous page to illustrate the poem.

VOCABULARY:

mower   one who cuts down a harvest

sower   one who plants a crop

furrows   trenches made in a field for planting

mystical   spiritual; mysterious; unknowable

yield   to give up; to give back; to give as a return for effort

ANALYZE:

1. What figure of speech is used throughout the first stanza? _____

  _____

2. What is the rhyme scheme of this poem? _____

  _____

COMPREHENSION QUESTIONS:

1. Explain the comparison being made in the first stanza. _____

_____

_____

_____

_____

2. What do the following symbolize?

   mowers:_____

   ripe old ears:_____

   sowers:_____

   tears: _____

3. Why would the furrows need to be "watered with tears"? _____

_____

_____

_____

_____

4. Think about the last two lines: "Life's field will yield as we make it, a harvest of thorns or of flowers."

   How would you interpret what the speaker is saying here? _____

_____

_____

_____

_____

_____

_____

_____

_____

_____

_____

ALL THINGS BRIGHT AND BEAUTIFUL

Cecil Frances Alexander

All things bright and beautiful,
    All creatures great and small,
All things wise and wonderful,
    The Lord God made them all.

Each little flower that opens,
    Each little bird that sings,
He made their glowing colors,
    He made their tiny wings.

The rich man in his castle,
    The poor man at his gate,
God made them, high or lowly,
    And ordered their estate.

The purple-headed mountain,
    The river running by,

The sunset, and the morning,
    That brightens up the sky;

The cold wind in the winter,
    The pleasant summer sun,
The ripe fruits in the garden,
    He made them every one.

The tall trees in the greenwood,
    The meadows where we play,
The rushes by the water,
    We gather every day;—

He gave us eyes to see them,
    And lips that we might tell,
How great is God Almighty,
    Who has made all things well.

COPYBOOK: Copy the poem in the space below. Use the box on the previous page to illustrate the poem.

VOCABULARY:

wise	having good sense and judgment; having wisdom
estate	all of a person's possessions
ripe	fully grown
rushes	plants that grow in marshy areas

ANALYZE:

1. Think about the rhyming structure of this poem. Label each line and then write out the rhyme scheme.

   _____

2. Underline an instance of personification in the poem.

1 All things bright and beautiful,   _____
2 All creatures great and small,   _____
3 All things wise and wonderful,   _____
4 The Lord God made them all.   _____

5 Each little flower that opens,   _____
6 Each little bird that sings,   _____
7 He made their glowing colors,   _____
8 He made their tiny wings.   _____

9 The rich man in his castle,   _____
10 The poor man at his gate,   _____
11 God made them, high or lowly,   _____
12 And ordered their estate.   _____

13 The purple-headed mountain,   _____
14 The river running by,   _____
15 The sunset, and the morning,   _____
16 That brightens up the sky;   _____

17 The cold wind in the winter,   _____
18 The pleasant summer sun,   _____
19 The ripe fruits in the garden,   _____
20 He made them every one.   _____

21 The tall trees in the greenwood,   _____
22 The meadows where we play,   _____
23 The rushes by the water,   _____
24 We gather every day;—   _____

25 He gave us eyes to see them,   _____
26 And lips that we might tell,   _____
27 How great is God Almighty,   _____
28 Who has made all things well.   _____

COMPREHENSION QUESTIONS:

1. From where does the poem say all things come? _____

_____

_____

_____

2. Why did God give us eyes and lips? _____

_____

_____

_____

3. What is the point of view of the first five stanzas? Of the last two? How do you know? _____

_____

_____

_____

_____

4. What are some bright and beautiful things you are thankful the Lord made? _____

_____

_____

_____

_____

_____

THE LAMB
William Blake

Little Lamb, who made thee?
Dost thou know who made thee?
Gave thee life, and bid thee feed,
By the stream and o'er the mead;
Gave thee clothing of delight,
Softest clothing, wooly, bright;
Gave thee such a tender voice,
Making all the vales rejoice!
Little Lamb, who made thee?
Dost thou know who made thee?

Little Lamb, I'll tell thee,
Little Lamb, I'll tell thee!
He is callèd by thy name,
For he calls himself a Lamb;
He is meek, and he is mild,
He became a little child;
I a child and thou a lamb,
We are callèd by his name.
Little Lamb, God bless thee!
Little Lamb, God bless thee!

COPYBOOK: Copy the poem in the space below. Use the box on the previous page to illustrate the poem.

_____

_____

_____

_____

_____

_____

_____

_____

_____

_____

_____

_____

_____

_____

_____

_____

_____

_____

_____

_____

_____

_____

_____

_____

_____

_____

_____

VOCABULARY:

bid	asked
mead	meadow
vale	valley
meek	quiet and gentle

ANALYZE:

1. Think about the rhyming structure of this poem. Label each line and then write out the rhyme scheme.

_____

1 Little Lamb, who made thee?   _____

2 Dost thou know who made thee?   _____

3 Gave thee life, and bid thee feed,   _____

4 By the stream and o'er the mead;   _____

5 Gave thee clothing of delight,   _____

6 Softest clothing, wooly, bright;   _____

7 Gave thee such a tender voice,   _____

8 Making all the vales rejoice!   _____

9 Little Lamb, who made thee?   _____

10 Dost thou know who made thee?   _____

11 Little Lamb, I'll tell thee,   _____

12 Little Lamb, I'll tell thee!   _____

13 He is callèd by thy name,   _____

14 For he calls himself a Lamb;   _____

15 He is meek, and he is mild,   _____

16 He became a little child;   _____

17 I a child and thou a lamb,   _____

18 We are callèd by his name.   _____

19 Little Lamb, God bless thee!   _____

20 Little Lamb, God bless thee!   _____

44   William Blake

COMPREHENSION QUESTIONS:

1. Whom is the speaker addressing?_____

_____

_____

_____

2. Whom is the speaker talking about when he says, "He is called by thy name, / For he calls himself a Lamb"?

_____

_____

_____

3. Who is the speaker?_____

_____

_____

_____

_____

4. What is a lamb's "clothing of delight"? _____

_____

_____

_____

5. What kinds of symbolism are associated with lambs? _____

_____

_____

_____

_____

_____

OUT IN THE FIELDS WITH GOD
Elizabeth Barrett Browning

The little cares that fretted me,
I lost them yesterday
Among the fields above the sea,
Among the winds at play;
Among the lowing of the herds,
The rustling of the trees;
Among the singing of the birds,
The humming of the bees.

The foolish fears of what might pass—
I cast them all away
Among the clover-scented grass,
Among the new-mown hay;
Among the husking of the corn,
Where drowsy poppies nod,
Where ill thoughts die and good are born,
Out in the fields with God.

COPYBOOK: Copy the poem in the space below. Use the box on the previous page to illustrate the poem.

VOCABULARY:

fretted	caused unease or worry
low	to utter the sound made by cattle; to moo
clover	a grass that blooms and attracts bees; also used for hay

ANALYZE:

1. Think about the rhyming structure of this poem. Label each line and then write out the rhyme scheme.

   _____

2. What literary devices do you notice in the poem? _____

   _____

   _____

1 The little cares that fretted me,   _____

2 I lost them yesterday   _____

3 Among the fields above the sea,   _____

4 Among the winds at play;   _____

5 Among the lowing of the herds,   _____

6 The rustling of the trees;   _____

7 Among the singing of the birds,   _____

8 The humming of the bees.   _____

9 The foolish fears of what might pass—   _____

10 I cast them all away   _____

11 Among the clover-scented grass,   _____

12 Among the new-mown hay;   _____

13 Among the husking of the corn,   _____

14 Where drowsy poppies nod,   _____

15 Where ill thoughts die and good are born,   _____

16 Out in the fields with God.   _____

COMPREHENSION QUESTIONS:

1. What are the examples of personification in this poem? _____

_____

_____

_____

_____

2. What is responsible for causing the author to fret? _____

_____

_____

3. Why are "fears of what might pass" foolish? _____

_____

_____

4. How do you cast fears away? _____

_____

_____

5. What are corn husks? _____

_____

_____

6. What are drowsy poppies? _____

_____

_____

_____

7. The author appeals to the senses in her imagery. What is seen? heard? felt? smelled? _____

_____

_____

_____

8. With what feeling does this poem leave you? _____

_____

_____

_____

THE GRASSHOPPER
The Greek of Anacreon
Translated by Abraham Cowley

Happy insect, what can be
In happiness compared to thee?
Fed with nourishment divine,
The dewy morning's gentle wine!
Nature waits upon thee still,
And thy verdant cup does fill;
Thou dost drink, and dance, and sing,
Happier than the happiest king!
All the fields which thou dost see,
All the plants belong to thee;
All the summer hours produce,
Fertile made with early juice.
Man for thee does sow and plow,
Farmer he, and landlord thou!

Thou dost innocently enjoy;
Nor does thy luxury destroy.
The shepherd gladly heareth thee,
More harmonious than he.
Thee country folk with gladness hear,
Prophet of the ripened year!
To thee, of all things upon earth,
Life is no longer than thy mirth.
Happy insect! happy thou,
Dost neither age nor winter know;
But when thou'st drunk, and danced, and sung
Thy fill, the flowery leaves among,
Sated with thy summer feast,
Thou retir'st to endless rest.

COPYBOOK: Copy the poem in the space below. Use the box on the previous page to illustrate the poem.

VOCABULARY:

divine	from God
verdant	green
fertile	productive
sated	appeased; satisfied to fullness
landlord	owner of the land
harmonious	musical
mirth	joy or happiness
retir'st	to withdraw

ANALYZE:

1. Underline all references to joy or happiness.

1 Happy insect, what can be
2 In happiness compared to thee?
3 Fed with nourishment divine,
4 The dewy morning's gentle wine!
5 Nature waits upon thee still,
6 And thy verdant cup does fill;
7 Thou dost drink, and dance, and sing,
8 Happier than the happiest king!
9 All the fields which thou dost see,
10 All the plants belong to thee;
11 All the summer hours produce,
12 Fertile made with early juice.
13 Man for thee does sow and plow,
14 Farmer he, and landlord thou!

15 Thou dost innocently enjoy;
16 Nor does thy luxury destroy.
17 The shepherd gladly heareth thee,
18 More harmonious than he.
19 Thee country folk with gladness hear,
20 Prophet of the ripened year!
21 To thee, of all things upon earth,
22 Life is no longer than thy mirth.
23 Happy insect! happy thou,
24 Dost neither age nor winter know;
25 But when thou'st drunk, and danced, and sung
26 Thy fill, the flowery leaves among,
27 Sated with thy summer feast,
28 Thou retir'st to endless rest.

COMPREHENSION QUESTIONS:

1. How does the author describe the grasshopper? _____

   _____

   _____

2. Why is the grasshopper such a happy insect? _____

   _____

   _____

3. What does the grasshopper eat and drink? From where does its food and drink come? _____

   _____

   _____

4. Why is the grasshopper happier than a king?_____

   _____

   _____

5. From the grasshopper's perspective, who owns everything it sees?_____

   _____

   _____

6. Who enjoys hearing the grasshopper? _____

   _____

   _____

7. How long does the grasshopper live? _____

   _____

   _____

8. Would you prefer a life like the grasshopper? Why or why not? _____

   _____

   _____

   _____

   _____

   _____

THERE IS NO FRIGATE LIKE A BOOK
Emily Dickinson

There is no frigate like a book,
To take us lands away,
Nor any coursers like a page
Of prancing poetry.

This traverse may the poorest take,
Without oppress of toll;
How frugal is the chariot
That bears a human soul.

COPYBOOK: Copy the poem in the space below. Use the box on the previous page to illustrate the poem.

VOCABULARY:

frigate   a warship with sails

coursers   swift horses or runners

traverse   a route or path across or over

oppress   to keep down by severe and unjust use of force or authority

toll   a fixed charge for a privilege, especially for passage across a bridge or along a road

frugal   costing little, inexpensive

ANALYZE:

1. Underline the similes.

2. List all the words that refer to books: _____

3. Write out an example of alliteration from the poem:_____

   _____

4. What is the literary device used in line 7? _____

1 There is no frigate like a book,

2 To take us lands away,

3 Nor any coursers like a page

4 Of prancing poetry.

5 This traverse may the poorest take,

6 Without oppress of toll;

7 How frugal is the chariot

8 That bears a human soul.

COMPREHENSION QUESTIONS:

1. How are books like frigates, coursers, and chariots? _____
   _____
   _____
   _____
   _____

2. What are some "lands" you have visited through books? _____
   _____
   _____
   _____
   _____

3. Why is poetry described with the adjective "prancing"? _____
   _____
   _____
   _____
   _____

4. What is required for this "traverse"? _____
   _____
   _____
   _____
   _____

5. Why are books considered frugal chariots? _____
   _____
   _____
   _____
   _____

I NEVER SAW A MOOR
Emily Dickinson

I never saw a moor
I never saw the sea;
Yet know I how the heather looks,
And what a wave must be.

I never spoke with God,
Nor visited in heaven;
Yet certain am I of the spot
As if the chart were given.

COPYBOOK: Copy the poem in the space below. Use the box on the previous page to illustrate the poem.

VOCABULARY:

moor   a broad area of open land with heather and peat bogs

heather   a low-growing evergreen shrub with small pinkish-purple flowers, found
                  commonly in Europe and Asia

chart   a map showing information used by navigators

ANALYZE:

1. Think about the rhyming structure of this poem. Label each line and then write out the rhyme scheme.

   _____

1 I never saw a moor   _____   5 I never spoke with God,   _____

2 I never saw the sea;   _____   6 Nor visited in heaven;   _____

3 Yet know I how the heather looks,   _____   7 Yet certain am I of the spot   _____

4 And what a wave must be.   _____   8 As if the chart were given.   _____

COMPREHENSION QUESTIONS:

1. Where are moors commonly found? Why might the speaker not have seen them?_____

_____

_____

_____

2. How does the speaker know about heather and waves if she has never seen them? _____

_____

_____

_____

3. Why might the order of the words in lines 3 and 7 be different from the first two lines in the stanzas?

_____

_____

_____

4. No one knows exactly where heaven is. What could the speaker mean in lines 7 and 8? _____

_____

_____

_____

5. How are God and heaven like the sea and the moor in this poem? _____

_____

_____

_____

TO THINK
Elizabeth Coatsworth

To think I once saw grocery shops
With but a casual eye
And figured figs and apricots
As one who came to buy.

To think I never dreamed of how
Bananas sway in rain

And often looked at oranges
And never thought of Spain.

And in those wasted days I saw
No sails above the tea,
For grocery shops were grocery shops—
Not hemispheres to me.

COPYBOOK: Copy the poem in the space below. Use the box on the previous page to illustrate the poem.

VOCABULARY:

apricot   a yellow-orange fruit

hemisphere   the Northern or Southern half of the earth as divided by the Equator; or the Eastern and Western half as divided by a meridian

ANALYZE:

1. Think about the rhyming structure of this poem. Label each line and then write out the rhyme scheme.

_____

1 To think I once saw grocery shops   _____

2 With but a casual eye   _____

3 And figured figs and apricots   _____

4 As one who came to buy.   _____

5 To think I never dreamed of how   _____

6 Bananas sway in rain   _____

7 And often looked at oranges   _____

8 And never thought of Spain.   _____

9 And in those wasted days I saw   _____

10 No sails above the tea,   _____

11 For grocery shops were grocery shops—   _____

12 Not hemispheres to me.   _____

COMPREHENSION QUESTIONS:

1. What emotion is the speaker expressing in the poem? What words show you the emotion?_____

   _____

   _____

   _____

2. Give a synonym for "casual," as used in the context of line 2. What does the speaker mean by "with but

   a casual eye"? _____

   _____

   _____

   _____

3. In the past, what was missing from trips to the grocery shop? What did the speaker not realize about

   bananas? oranges? _____

   _____

   _____

   _____

   _____

4. Why should she have seen "sails above the tea"? _____

   _____

   _____

   _____

5. Now that the speaker's eyes have been opened, what is a trip to the grocery shop like? _____

   _____

   _____

   _____

6. Do you ever think of where your food comes from, who planted it, what hands picked it, or who

   brought it to your store? What can you now wonder about when you walk through the grocery store?

   _____

   _____

   _____

*Questions for this poem contributed by Mrs. Cheryl Lowe.

SHAKER POEM
Unknown Author

A man of kindness to his beast is kind.
Brutal actions show a brutal mind.
Remember, He who made the brute,
Who gave thee speech and reason, formed him mute;
He can't complain; but God's omniscient eye
Beholds thy cruelty. He hears his cry.
He was destined thy servant and thy drudge,
But know this: His creator is thy judge.

COPYBOOK: Copy the poem in the space below. Use the box on the previous page to illustrate the poem.

VOCABULARY:

beast	an animal
brutal	cruel; ruthless
brute	an animal; a beast
mute	unable to speak
omniscient	knowing everything
destined	determined beforehand
drudge	a person who does menial work

ANALYZE:

1. Think about the rhyming structure of this poem. Label each line and then write out the rhyme scheme.

   _____

2. Underline the two imperative verbs in this poem (verbs that command).

1   A man of kindness to his beast is kind.   _____

2   Brutal actions show a brutal mind.   _____

3   Remember, He who made the brute,   _____

4   Who gave thee speech and reason, formed him mute;   _____

5   He can't complain; but God's omniscient eye   _____

6   Beholds thy cruelty. He hears his cry.   _____

7   He was destined thy servant and thy drudge,   _____

8   But know this: His creator is thy judge.   _____

COMPREHENSION QUESTIONS:

1. What commands does the poem give the reader? _____

_____

_____

_____

2. Who is "He" in line 3?_____

_____

_____

_____

3. Why might you forget to treat animals with kindness? How does the speaker help us remember to

be kind? _____

_____

_____

_____

_____

4. What are some ways animals serve humans as "drudges"?_____

_____

_____

_____

5. Read Proverbs 12:10. How does that verse relate to this poem? _____

_____

_____

_____

THE NIGHTINGALE AND THE GLOW-WORM

William Cowper

A nightingale, that all day long
Had cheered the village with his song,
Nor yet at eve his note suspended,
Nor yet when eventide was ended,
Began to feel—as well he might—
The keen demands of appetite;
When, looking eagerly around,
He spied, far off, upon the ground,
A something shining in the dark,
And knew the glow-worm by his spark;
So, stooping down from hawthorn top,
He thought to put him in his crop.
The worm, aware of his intent,
Harangued him thus, quite eloquent—
"Did you admire my lamp," quoth he,
"As much as I your minstrelsy,
You would abhor to do me wrong,
As much as I to spoil your song;
For 'twas the self-same Power divine
Taught you to sing and me to shine;
That you with music, I with light,
Might beautify and cheer the night."
The songster heard his short oration,
And, warbling out his approbation,
Released him, as my story tells,
And found a supper somewhere else.

COPYBOOK: Copy the poem in the space below. Use the box on the previous page to illustrate the poem.

VOCABULARY:

eve, eventide	evening
keen	sharp; strong
hawthorn	a thorny tree or shrub
crop	a pouch in a bird's throat for storing food
intent	aim or purpose
harangue	a long, pompous speech; a tirade
eloquent	vividly moving or expressive
minstrelsy	the art of musical entertainment
abhor	to detest, loathe
warbling	singing
approbation	warm approval; praise

ANALYZE:

1. Think about the rhyming structure of this poem. Label each line and then write out the rhyme scheme.

_____

1 A nightingale, that all day long   _____

2 Had cheered the village with his song,   _____

3 Nor yet at eve his note suspended,   _____

4 Nor yet when eventide was ended,   _____

5 Began to feel—as well he might—   _____

6 The keen demands of appetite;   _____

7 When, looking eagerly around,   _____

8 He spied, far off, upon the ground,   _____

9 A something shining in the dark,   _____

10 And knew the glow-worm by his spark;   _____

11 So, stooping down from hawthorn top,   _____

12 He thought to put him in his crop.   _____

13 The worm, aware of his intent,   _____

14 Harangued him thus, quite eloquent—   _____

15 "Did you admire my lamp," quoth he,   _____

16 "As much as I your minstrelsy,   _____

17 You would abhor to do me wrong,   _____

18 As much as I to spoil your song;   _____

19 For 'twas the self-same Power divine   _____

20 Taught you to sing and me to shine;   _____

21 That you with music, I with light,   _____

22 Might beautify and cheer the night."   _____

23 The songster heard his short oration,   _____

24 And, warbling out his approbation,   _____

25 Released him, as my story tells,   _____

26 And found a supper somewhere else.   _____

COMPREHENSION QUESTIONS:

1. Summarize the story of the poem in your own words. _____

_____

_____

_____

_____

_____

_____

_____

_____

2. What causes the nightingale to go so long without food?_____

_____

_____

3. How long is the nightingale without food?_____

_____

_____

4. Rephrase "keen demands of appetite" in your own words._____

_____

_____

5. Explain the glow-worm's argument. _____

_____

_____

_____

_____

6. Who is the "self-same Power divine"? How do you know?_____

_____

_____

7. Does the glow-worm's speech achieve its purpose? _____

_____

_____

THE BAREFOOTED FRIAR
Sir Walter Scott

I'll give thee, good fellow, a twelvemonth or twain,
To search Europe through, from Byzantium to Spain;
But ne'er shall you find, should you search till
    you tire,
So happy a man as the Barefooted Friar.

Your knight for his lady pricks forth in career,
And is brought home at even-song prick'd
    through with a spear;
I confess him in haste—for his lady desires
No comfort on earth save the Barefooted Friar's.

Your monarch?—Pshaw! many a prince has
    been known
To barter his robes for our cowl and our gown,
But which of us e'er felt the idle desire
To exchange for a crown the grey hood of a Friar!

The Friar has walk'd out, and where'er he has gone,
The land and its fatness is mark'd for his own;

He can roam where he lists, he can stop when
    he tires,
For every man's house is the Barefooted Friar's.

He's expected at noon, and no wight till he comes
May profane the great chair, or the porridge of plums
For the best of the cheer, and the seat by the fire,
Is the undenied right of the Barefooted Friar.

He's expected at night, and the pasty's made hot,
They broach the brown ale, and they fill the
    black pot,
And the goodwife would wish the goodman in
    the mire,
Ere he lack'd a soft pillow, the Barefooted Friar.

Long flourish the sandal, the cord, and the cope,
The dread of the devil and trust of the Pope;
For to gather life's roses, unscathed by the briar,
Is granted alone to the Barefooted Friar.

COPYBOOK: Copy the poem in the space below. Use the box on the previous page to illustrate the poem.

VOCABULARY:

twain	two	**pasty**	a round of pastry folded over a filling of meat, vegetables, etc.
confess	to acknowledge and admit sin	**broach**	to draw off a liquid by piercing a hole in a container
barter	to trade		
cowl	a hooded garment worn by monks	**mire**	an area of wet, swampy ground
wight	a human being	**unscathed**	unharmed, uninjured
profane	to violate the sanctity of		

ANALYZE:

1. What is the rhyming structure of this poem? _____

2. What is the refrain in this poem? _____

1   I'll give thee, good fellow, a twelvemonth or twain,

2   To search Europe through, from Byzantium to Spain;

3   But ne'er shall you find, should you search till you tire,

4   So happy a man as the Barefooted Friar.

5   Your knight for his lady pricks forth in career,

6   And is brought home at even-song prick'd through with a spear;

7   I confess him in haste—for his lady desires

8   No comfort on earth save the Barefooted Friar's.

9   Your monarch?—Pshaw! many a prince has been known

10   To barter his robes for our cowl and our gown,

11   But which of us e'er felt the idle desire

12   To exchange for a crown the grey hood of a Friar!

13   The Friar has walk'd out, and where'er he has gone,

14   The land and its fatness is mark'd for his own;

15   He can roam where he lists, he can stop when he tires,

16   For every man's house is the Barefooted Friar's.

17   He's expected at noon, and no wight till he comes

18   May profane the great chair, or the porridge of plums

19   For the best of the cheer, and the seat by the fire,

20   Is the undenied right of the Barefooted Friar.

21   He's expected at night, and the pasty's made hot,

22   They broach the brown ale, and they fill the black pot,

23   And the goodwife would wish the goodman in the mire,

24   Ere he lack'd a soft pillow, the Barefooted Friar.

25   Long flourish the sandal, the cord, and the cope,

26   The dread of the devil and trust of the Pope;

27   For to gather life's roses, unscathed by the briar,

28   Is granted alone to the Barefooted Friar.

COMPREHENSION QUESTIONS:

1. What is a friar? _____

_____

_____

2. What is meant by the phrase "from Byzantium to Spain"? _____

_____

_____

3. To whom is the friar compared? How does he fare in comparison? _____

_____

_____

4. Why doesn't the friar desire the king's crown? _____

_____

_____

5. What "rights" does the friar have? _____

_____

_____

6. How do the people treat the friar? _____

_____

_____

7. To what do "the sand, the cord, and the cope" refer? _____

_____

_____

8. What is meant by "to gather life's roses, unscathed by the briar"? _____

_____

_____

TIME, YOU OLD GYPSY MAN

Ralph Hodgson

Time, you old gypsy man,
Will you not stay,
Put up your caravan
Just for one day?

All things I'll give you
Will you be my guest,
Bells for your jennet
Of silver the best,
Goldsmiths shall beat you
A great golden ring,
Peacocks shall bow to you
Little boys sing.
Oh, and sweet girls will
Festoon you with may.
Time, you old gypsy,
Why hasten away?

Last week in Babylon,
Last night in Rome,
Morning, and in the crush
Under Paul's dome;
Under Paul's dial
You tighten your rein—
Only a moment,
And off once again;
Off to some city
Now blind in the womb,
Off to another
Ere that's in the tomb.

Time, you old gypsy man,
Will you not stay,
Put up your caravan
Just for one day?

COPYBOOK: Copy the poem in the space below. Use the box on the previous page to illustrate the poem.

VOCABULARY:

jennet	a small spanish saddle horse
festoon	to decorate with garland
may	the blossoms of the hawthorn
ere	before

ANALYZE:

1. What is the refrain of this poem? _____

_____

_____

1 Time, you old gypsy man,

2 Will you not stay,

3 Put up your caravan

4 Just for one day?

5 All things I'll give you

6 Will you be my guest,

7 Bells for your jennet

8 Of silver the best,

9 Goldsmiths shall beat you

10 A great golden ring,

11 Peacocks shall bow to you

12 Little boys sing.

13 Oh, and sweet girls will

14 Festoon you with may.

15 Time, you old gypsy,

16 Why hasten away?

17 Last week in Babylon,

18 Last night in Rome,

19 Morning, and in the crush

20 Under Paul's dome;

21 Under Paul's dial

22 You tighten your rein—

23 Only a moment,

24 And off once again;

25 Off to some city

26 Now blind in the womb,

27 Off to another

28 Ere that's in the tomb.

29 Time, you old gypsy man,

30 Will you not stay,

31 Put up your caravan

32 Just for one day?

COMPREHENSION QUESTIONS:

1. What kind of lifestyle do gypsies lead? _____

   _____

   _____

2. What things does the speaker promise to give Time if he stays? Do these seem like gifts that would

   tempt Time to stay? _____

   _____

   _____

   _____

3. Rephrase "of silver the best" in prose. _____

   _____

   _____

4. What are the places Time visits? _____

   _____

   _____

5. To what do "Paul's dome" and "Paul's dial" refer? What would be the "crush" under them? _____

   _____

   _____

6. What is the imagery in line 22? _____

   _____

   _____

   _____

7. How does the speaker feel about Time? Why do you think he wants Time to stay? _____

   _____

   _____

   _____

8. What is the theme of this poem? _____

   _____

   _____

   _____

ENGLAND'S SOVEREIGNS IN VERSE
English Ballad

Norman Kings (1066)
William the Conqueror long did reign,
William, his son, by an arrow was slain;
Henry the First was a scholar bright;
Stephen was king without any right.

Plantagenet
Henry the Second, Plantagenet's scion;
Richard the First was brave as a lion;
John, though a tyrant, the Charter signed;
Henry the Third had a weakly mind.

Edward the First conquered Cambria dales;
Edward the Second was born Prince of Wales;
Edward the Third humbled France in its pride;
Richard the Second in prison died.

House of Lancaster
Henry the Fourth for himself took the crown;
Henry the Fifth pulled the French king down;
Henry the Sixth lost his father's gains.

House of Tudor
Edward of York laid hold of the reins
Edward the Fifth was killed with his brother;
Richard the Third soon made way for another.
Henry the Seventh was frugal of means;

Henry the Eighth had a great many queens.
Edward the Sixth reformation began;

Then Queen Mary prevented the plan.
Wise and profound were Elizabeth's aims.

Stuart Line
England and Scotland were joined by King James.
Charles found the people a cruel corrector;
Oliver Cromwell was called Lord Protector;

Charles the Second was hid in an oak;
James the Second was for Catholic folk;
William and Mary were offered the throne,
Anne succeeded and reigned alone.

Hanovarian
George the First from Hanover came;
George the Second kept up the name;
George the Third was loved in the land,
George the Fourth was pompous and grand,

William the Fourth had no heir of his own, So
Queen Victoria ascended the throne.
When good Queen Victoria's long reign was o'er
Edward the Seventh the English crown wore.

George the Fifth kept a strict moral tone;
Edward VIII relinquished the throne;
George VI through the war years was king;
Of Elizabeth II her praises we sing,
All her subjects declaring,
"God Save the Queen!"

Use the box below to illustrate the poem.

VOCABULARY:

tyrant   an absolute ruler; usually wields power oppressively

frugal   spending resources sparingly and wisely; thrifty

profound   having intellectual depth; deep insight; going beneath the superficial

pompous   full of self-importance; stately

relinquished   gave up; renounced

HISTORY OF THE ENGLISH MONARCHY:

William I: Also known as William the Conqueror, he was one of several contenders for the English throne when the previous king, Edward the Confessor, died childless. In 1066, William and his army invaded England, killing another contender for the throne at the Battle of Hastings, and claiming the throne of England. He ruled for over twenty years, from **1066-1087**.

William II: Also known as William Rufus, he reigned from **1087-1100**. He was the second of William I's three sons. He died of an arrow wound while hunting.

Henry I: Third son of William the Conqueror, he reigned from **1100-1135**. He was known for his interest in scholarship, and his judicial and financial reforms.

Stephen of Blois: Henry I's son had drowned in a shipwreck, leaving no apparent heir, and leaving the matter of succession open to challenge. Henry had forced his barons to profess loyalty to his daughter Matilda, and establish her as queen on his death, but Stephen of Blois (a grandson of William the Conqueror) raised an army and took the throne for himself. This led to civil war between Matilda and Stephen, a period known as The Anarchy. The war ended with the Treaty of Wallingford, which established Matilda's son Henry II (a grandson of Henry I) as king.

Henry II: The first of the Plantagenets to sit on the English throne, a grandson of Henry I. After years of civil war he had to re-establish the authority of the English throne when he took power.

Richard I: The son of Henry II, he was known as Richard the Lionheart. He spent very little of his reign in England, the rest spent in the Holy Lands trying to reclaim Jerusalem as part of the Third Crusade. He reigned from **1189-1199**.

John: Son of Henry II and younger brother of Richard the Lionheart, he inherited the throne on the death of his brother in **1199**, and reigned until **1216**. Some of his powerful nobles were unhappy with John's treatment of them, and other policies, and they forced him to sign the Magna Carta in 1215, a document that limited the king's absolute power, making him subject to and bound by certain laws. John has also been made famous as the "Prince John" of the Robin Hood stories.

Henry III: Son of John, Henry III inherited the throne at the age of nine under a regency. Even as he grew old enough to reign in his own right, he was weak-minded, and controlled by his nobles and ministers. He was forced to sign the Provisions of Oxford in 1258, a document that built on the Magna Carta and wrested even more power from the monarchy. Henry III reigned from **1216-1272**.

Edward I: Son of Henry III, he reigned from **1272-1307**. A rebellious uprising in Wales led him to launch a full-scale war of conquest, subjecting Wales to English rule.

Edward II: Son of Edward I, he reigned from **1307-1327**. As his father had successfully conquered Wales, Edward II inherited the title of Prince of Wales, a title that almost all heirs apparent to the English throne have been granted since then. He was deposed by his wife and son, Edward III.

Edward III: Son of Edward II, he reigned from **1327-1377**. He was crowned king at age 15, under the regency of his mother and Lord Mortimer until the end of his minority. His aggression towards French lands, and claim to the French throne in 1340, began a war between England and France (called the Hundred Years War) that would last, off and on, until 1453. Edward won many victories on French soil, claiming French cities, but was often forced to release them back to the French or sign treaties because of lack of funding to continue campaigns. Edward's son, the Black Prince of Wales, captured the King of France during the battle of Poitiers.

Richard II: Grandson of Edward III (son of the Black Prince of Wales, who died young), he reigned from **1377-1399**. His reign was marked by instability and power struggles between Richard, the Parliament, and English nobles. Richard was finally forced to abdicate his throne in 1399, and died in prison. The man who took his throne was another grandson of Edward III, and the first ruler of the House of Lancaster, Henry IV.

Henry IV: A cousin of Richard II, and grandson of Edward III, Henry IV reigned from **1399-1413**. He came to the throne by deposing his cousin Richard II.

Henry V: Son of Henry IV, he reigned from **1413-1422**. He continued the Hundred Years War with France, claiming that the English had historical claim to certain French cities, and legitimate claim to the throne of France. He led many successful campaigns in France, the most famous of which was the Battle of Agincourt. His victories led to the Treaty of Toyes, in which the French king Charles VI named Henry V his heir and Regent of France, and the daughter of the French king was given to Henry in marriage.

Henry VI: The only child of Henry V and Catherine, the daughter of the French king. When King Charles VI of France died, Henry was proclaimed king of France according to the Treaty of Troyes, but Henry did not campaign in France like his father, nor did he work hard to keep the lands his father had won, and they were slowly taken back by the French. Henry's cousin Richard, Duke of York, had a stronger claim to the English throne through lines of succession, and his attempts to take the throne set off the War of the Roses (English civil war between the Yorks and the Lancasters for the throne). Henry was finally forced to agree that in place of his own son, the Duke of York would succeed to the throne on his death. When the elder Duke was killed in battle, the succession passed to his son. In 1461 Henry VI was decisively beaten in battle and fled the country, and the young Duke of York was proclaimed King Edward IV. In 1470 Henry landed in England with an army to take back the throne, which he held until 1471 when Edward took it back. Henry VI was killed in the tower of London. He reigned from **1422-1461**, and again from **1470-1471**.

Edward IV: The first in the line of Yorks who held the English throne, he claimed the right to rule through descent from sons of Edward III, and took the throne by force from Henry VI. He reigned from **1461-1470**, and again from **1471-1483** after he took the throne from Henry VI for the second time.

Edward V: Son of Edward IV, he reigned from **April to June 1483**. He ascended the throne at the age of 12, with his uncle (Edward IV's brother) Richard named as Protector of the Realm until Edward V should reach the end of his minority. Richard took possession of Edward and his younger brother and stashed them in the Tower of London, where they appeared less and less to the public. It is widely believed that they were murdered in either the summer or fall of 1483.

Richard III: Brother of Edward IV, Richard claimed that Edward IV's marriage had been invalid, and thus Edward V was an illegitimate heir. He took the throne for himself in **1483**, asserting that he had the legitimate claim to the throne. He reigned for only two years before he was defeated at the Battle of Bosworth Field in **1485** by Henry Tudor, officially ending the War of the Roses.

Henry VII: Also known as Henry Tudor, he was the first of the House of Tudor to sit on the English throne. He defeated Richard III at the Battle of Bosworth Field to claim the throne. Henry refrained from waging expensive wars that would drain the crown's finances, and instead focused on developing trade and marital alliances to increase the prosperity of the country.

Henry VIII: The second son of Henry VII, he reigned from **1509-1547**. Henry had six wives over the course of his reign. His first wife, Catherine of Aragon, was a Spanish princess who bore to Henry one daughter (Mary, later to be known as Mary I or Bloody Mary), but no male heirs. Henry eventually had his marriage to Catherine annulled in order to marry his second wife, Anne Boleyn. Anne bore one daughter (Elizabeth), but also had no male heirs. After several miscarriages, Henry had Anne executed, for allegations of treasonable adultery, so that he would be free to marry his third wife, Jane Seymour. Jane bore Henry his only son, Edward, and died shortly after childbirth from complications. Henry then married Anne of Cleves, having never seen her before the wedding, and shortly had the marriage annulled. His fifth wife was Catherine Howard, a twenty-year-old woman whose affairs with other men after her marriage to Henry led to her execution. Henry's sixth and final wife was Catherine Parr, a wealthy widow.

Edward VI: Henry VIII's son by Jane Seymour, he reigned from **1547-1553**. As he was only nine years old at the time he ascended the throne, and fifteen when he died, the country was governed by a Regency Council for his entire reign. Though he was young, Edward was devoutly Protestant, and with the help of his ministers, began instituting the Protestant Reformation in England.

Mary I: The daughter of Henry VIII and Catherine of Aragon, she reigned from **1553-1558**. Mary was the first woman to hold the English throne in her own right. Her half-brother Edward had tried to remove her from the line of succession because of her staunchly Catholic beliefs, and fear that she would undo all the work he had begun in reforming the Church of England. His fears were well founded, as immediately upon her succession, she reversed Edward's reforms and restored Roman Catholicism as the state religion of England. She put down a Protestant rebellion in 1554, and continued to persecute Protestants throughout her reign, hunting down and executing many, and forcing hundreds to flee into exile. She earned the nickname Bloody Mary for her actions.

Elizabeth I: Daughter of Henry VIII and Anne Boleyn, she reigned from **1158-1603**. She succeeded after the death of her half-sister Mary, who died childless. Threat of a Catholic revolt haunted her reign, provoked by the belief held by some of her subjects that Mary, Queen of Scots (the passionately Catholic queen of Scotland), had a better claim to the English throne, and also by an influx of Jesuit missionaries into England during her reign. Elizabeth thwarted several rebellions and had many of the Jesuits hunted down and executed for treason. The period of her reign is known in English history as the Elizabethan Era, or the Golden Age. It was a period when art, literature, theater, science, trade, and exploration flourished. Elizabeth asserted her right to govern and participate in the affairs of state, and did not let others take from her the power to make crucial decisions or shape policies. She never married, is often referred to as the Virgin Queen, and left no heirs.

James I: Elizabeth had no children, and so on her death, the English throne passed to King James VI of Scotland, descendant of Henry VII. He became James I, King of England, Ireland, and Scotland. He reigned from **1603-1625** as the first of the Stuart line. He called himself the King of Great Britain and Ireland.

Charles I: Son of James I, he reigned from **1625-1649**. From the beginning of his reign, Charles experienced conflicts with Parliament. Only the king could call a session of Parliament, but once called, Parliament had a great deal of power. They became more and more critical of Charles' government, and more radical in demands. The struggle between Charles and his supporters (Royalists) and Parliament and their supporters (Parliamentarians) led to the English Civil Wars. Eventually Charles was captured, charged with high treason, and executed.

Oliver Cromwell: After Charles I had been deposed and executed, England was declared a Commonwealth under the rule of Parliament. In **1653** Oliver Cromwell, celebrated veteran of the Civil Wars, was proclaimed Lord Protector of the Commonwealth. He was offered the crown by Parliament, but refused it. The role of Protector was not hereditary, though he was allowed to choose his own successor. He chose his son to succeed him, but the Commonwealth began to collapse soon after his death.

Charles II: The son of Charles I. After his father's death, he eluded capture (once by hiding in the Royal Oak Tree at Bobscobel House) and fled to the Netherlands. When the Commonwealth began to fall apart after the death of Oliver Cromwell, Parliament invited Charles II back to England and offered him the crown, restoring the monarchy. The period of his reign (**1660-1685**) is commonly referred to as the Restoration.

James II: Brother of Charles II, who died without any legitimate heirs, James II inherited the throne on his brother's death and reigned from **1685-1688**. While his brother was still king, he had converted to Roman Catholicism, which caused alarm among predominantly Protestant England when it became clear James II would be the heir apparent. When he came to the throne it seemed that his would be a reign of religious tolerance, but after having to quell several rebellions, he began to distrust his subjects. He began appointing men who were openly Catholic to positions of power, alienating those of Protestant faith. When a son was born to James and his second wife, the prospect of a Roman Catholic succession prompted prominent Protestants in James' government to take action. Several politicians had been communicating with the husband of James' daughter Mary (William of Orange), a defender of Protestantism in Europe, and eventually sent him a formal invitation to invade and take the throne from James. When James learned of the plot, he assumed it would be easy to repel the invasion, but did not count on his Protestant officers deserting en masse to William's cause when he landed in England. James was deposed by William and Mary in 1688.

William III and Mary II: William of Orange and his wife Mary (daughter of James II) were invited by a group of politicians in James' government to invade and take the throne from James when the birth of his son made real the possibility of a Roman Catholic heir to the throne. William and Mary landed in England and claimed the throne with relatively little military resistance (many of the Protestant officers in James' army defected), and were crowned joint king and queen of England, in what is known as the Glorious Revolution. The crown was offered conditionally: the crown would no longer have the power to suspend laws, would not be able to keep a standing army during times of peace, and a Bill of Rights was passed by Parliament that further limited the powers of the monarchs, and established Parliament as the governing power of England. The king and queen retained some of the former power of English monarchs, but would have to rule through Parliament. Mary reigned from **1689-1694** when she died of smallpox, and William reigned from **1689-1702**. As neither William and Mary, nor the heir apparent, Anne (daughter of James I), had any living children in 1701, there was panic of a succession crisis should Anne die heirless. The Act of Settlement 1701 passed a law that, failing the birth of heirs by William and Mary or Anne, the crown would pass to the descendants of King James I through his daughter Elizabeth. Heirs of Roman Catholic faith were prohibited by law from inheriting the throne.

Anne: Daughter of James II, but raised Protestant, Anne reigned from **1702-1714**. She married Prince George of Denmark, but Anne and George were not co-rulers like William and Mary; Anne ruled alone, with the aid of her ministers.

George I: Through the Act of Settlement, George, the Elector of Hanover (Germany), and a great-grandson of James I, was appointed Anne's successor, and reigned from **1714-1727**. He spoke no English, and had to communicate with his minsters by speaking French.

George II: The only son of George I, he reigned from **1727-1760**. He was very interested and involved in the politics of the realm early in his reign, but less and less so towards the end.

George III: Grandson of George II, he reigned from **1760-1820**. He was the first Hanovarian monarch to be born in England and speak English as his first language. He inherited the throne in the middle of the Seven Years War, and his reign was marked by political instability, war, and financial difficulties. The American Revolution took place during his reign (1775-1783), as well as war with Napoleon. He was alternately hated and loved by the populace throughout his reign, but towards the end of it he was looked upon favorably as a symbol of national resistance against Napoleon.

George IV: George III suffered intermittent bouts of insanity at the end of his life, and Regency powers were given to his son George IV starting in 1811. He was officially crowned king in **1820** on his father's death, and reigned until **1830**. Fond of drinking and women and spending money, George was charming and well educated, but his behavior often reflected poorly on the crown.

William IV: Son of George III and younger brother of George IV, William IV was 64 years old when he inherited the crown. He reigned from **1830-1837**. He had no legitimate children, and on his death the throne passed to Victoria, his niece and granddaughter of George III.

Victoria: Niece of William IV and granddaughter of George III, she reigned from **1837-1901**, the second-longest reign of any English Monarch (63 years). Her reign is called the Victorian Era, and was a time of scientific, social, industrial, and political change. The role of the monarchy in governing the country became even more limited over the course of Victoria's reign.

Edward VII: The eldest son of Victoria, he reigned from **1901-1910**. He was incredibly popular with the English public, and through the descendants of Victoria was related to almost every monarch in Europe at the time.

George V: The son of Edward VII, he reigned from **1910-1936**. His reign encompassed WWI (1914-1918), a conflict that embroiled all of Europe and eventually America in a war that had catastrophically high casualties. George V led a moderate lifestyle, remaining faithful to his wife throughout their marriage, and preferring to stay at home and pursue his hobbies.

Edward VIII: The son of George V, he reigned from **January to December 1936**. Before his succession he had fallen in love with a twice-divorced American socialite (Wallis Simpson), and made it clear after his succession that he intended to marry her. The possibility of Wallis becoming queen caused a panic in England for religious, political, and social reasons, and the Parliament threatened to retire en masse (leaving the government in crisis) if Edward went through with the wedding. Instead of giving up Wallis, he abdicated the throne less than a year after his succession in order to marry her, passing the crown to his younger brother George VI.

George VI: The son of George V, and younger brother of Edward VIII, he inherited the throne after Edward abdicated, and reigned from **1936-1952**. George developed strong ties with France, the U.S., and other countries who would become allies during WWII (1939-1945).

Elizabeth II: Daughter of George VI, she is the current queen of England and has been on the throne since **1952**. She is currently the longest reigning English monarch. "God Save the Queen" is the national anthem of Great Britain.

ROBIN HOOD AND THE RANGER
Anonymous English Ballad

When Phoebus had melted the sickles of ice,
And likewise the mountains of snow,
Bold Robin Hood he would ramble to see,
To frolick abroad with his bow.

He left all his merry men waiting behind,
Whilst through the green valleys he passed;
There did he behold a forester bold,
Who cried out, "Friend, whither so fast?"

"I'm going," quoth Robin Hood, "to kill a fat buck,
For me and my merry men all;
Besides, e'er I go, I'll have a fat doe,
Or else it shall cost me a fall."

"You'd best have a care," said the forester then,
"For these are his majesty's deer;
Before you shall shoot, the thing I'll dispute,
For I am head-forester here."

"These thirteen long summers," quoth Robin,
    "I'm sure,
My arrows I here have let fly,
Where freely I range; methinks it is strange,
You should have more power than I."

"This forest," quoth Robin, "I think is my own,
And so are the nimble deer too;
Therefore I declare, and solemnly swear,
I won't be affronted by you."

The forester he had a long quarter-staff,
Likewise a broad sword by his side;
Without more ado, he presently drew,
Declaring the truth should be tried.

Bold Robin Hood had a sword of the best,
Thus, ere he would take any wrong,
His courage was flush, he'd venture a brush,
And thus they fell to it ding-dong.

The very first blow that the forester gave,
He made his broad weapon cry twang;
'Twas over the head, he fell down for dead,
O that was a terrible bang!

But Robin soon did recover himself,
And bravely fell to it again;
The very next stroke their weapons were broke,
Yet never a man there was slain.

At quarter-staff then they resolved to play,
Because they would have t'other bout;
And brave Robin Hood right valiantly stood,
Unwilling he was to give out.

Bold Robin he gave him very hard blows,
The other returned them as fast;
At every stroke their jackets did smoke,
Three hours the combat did last.

At length in a rage the bold forester grew,
And cudgeled bold Robin so sore
That he could not stand, so shaking his hand,
He said, "Let us freely give o'er."

"Thou art a brave fellow, I needs must confess,
I never knew any so good;
Thou 'rt fitting to be a yeoman for me,
And range in the merry green wood."

"I'll give thee this ring as a token of love,
For bravely thou'st acted thy part;
That man that can fight, in him I delight,
And love him with all my whole heart."

Then Robin Hood, setting his horn to his mouth,
A blast he merrily blows;
His yeomen did hear, and straight did appear,
A hundred with trusty long bows.

Now Little John came at the head of them all,
Clothed in a rich mantle of green;
And likewise the rest were gloriously drest,
A right gallant sight to be seen.

"Lo, these are my yeomen," said Robin Hood,
"And thou shalt be one of the train;
A mantle and bow, a quiver also,
I give them whom I entertain

The forester willingly entered the list,
They were such a beautiful sight;
Then with a long bow they shot a fat doe,
And made a rich supper that night.

What singing and dancing was in the green wood,
For joy of another new mate!
With mirth and delight they spent the long night,
And lived at a plentiful rate.

Robin Hood gave him a mantle of green,
Broad arrows and a very long bow;
This done, the next day, so gallant and gay,
He marched them all on a row.

Quoth he, "My brave yeomen, be true to your trust,
And then we may range the woods wide."
They all did declare and solemnly swear,
They'd conquer, or die by his side.

COPYBOOK: Copy select parts of the poem in the space below. Use the box on the previous page to illustrate the poem.

_____

_____

_____

_____

_____

_____

_____

_____

_____

_____

_____

_____

_____

_____

_____

_____

_____

_____

_____

_____

_____

_____

_____

_____

_____

_____

_____

VOCABULARY:

Phoebus	the Greek god Apollo, as the sun-god
frolick (frolic)	to play or run about merrily
dispute	to argue; to protest; to oppose
nimble	quick; light; agile
cudgeled	beat
gallant	noble; chivalrous; grand; brave
mirth	joy; amusement

ANALYZE:

1. Think about the rhyming structure of this poem. Write out the rhyme scheme. _____

   _____

2. Summarize the story of the poem. _____

   _____

   _____

   _____

   _____

   _____

   _____

   _____

   _____

   _____

   _____

   _____

   _____

   _____

   _____

   _____

COMPREHENSION QUESTIONS:

1. To whom is the head forester loyal at the beginning of the poem? At the end? _____

_____

_____

_____

_____

_____

2. Why do you think the forester chooses to go with Robin Hood? _____

_____

_____

_____

_____

_____

3. Consider how quickly the ranger accepts Robin Hood's offer. What does this say about his commitment

to his position as head forester? _____

_____

_____

_____

_____

_____

4. At the end of the poem, all the Merry Men swear that they will "conquer, or die by [Robin's] side." What

is it about Robin that inspires his men to have such loyalty to him? _____

_____

_____

_____

_____

_____

THE WOOING OF SIR KEITH
Howard Pyle

King Arthur sat in his royal hall,
    And about on either hand
Was many a noble lordling tall,
    The greatest in the land.

Sat Lancelot with raven locks,
    Gawaine with golden hair,
Sir Tristram, Kay who kept the locks,
    And many another there.

And through the stained windows bright,
    From o'er the red-tiled eaves,
The sunlight blazed with colored light
    On golden helms and greaves.

But suddenly a silence came
    About the Table Round,
For up the hall there walked a dame
    Bent nigh unto the ground.

Her nose was hooked, her eyes were bleared,
    Her locks were lank and white;
Upon her chin there grew a beard;
    She was a gruesome sight.

And so with crawling step she came
    And kneeled at Arthur's feet;
Quoth Kay, 'She is the foulest dame
    That e'er my sight did greet.'

'O mighty King! of thee I crave
    A boon on bended knee';
'Twas thus she spoke. 'What wouldst thou have.'
    Quoth Arthur, King, 'of me?'

Quoth she, 'I have a foul disease
    Doth gnaw my very heart,
And but one thing can bring me ease
    Or cure my bitter smart.

'There is no rest, no ease for me
    North, east, or west, or south,
Till Christian knight will willingly
    Thrice kiss me on the mouth.

'Nor wedded may this childe have been
    That giveth ease to me;
Nor may he be constrained, I ween,
    But kiss me willingly.

'So is there here one Christian knight
    Of such a noble strain
That he will give a tortured wight
    Sweet ease of mortal pain?'

'A wedded man,' quoth Arthur, King,
    A wedded man I be
Else would I deem it noble thing
    To kiss thee willingly.

'Now, Lancelot, in all men's sight
    Thou art the head and chief
Of chivalry. Come, noble knight,
    And give her quick relief.'

But Lancelot he turned aside
    And looked upon the ground,
For it did sting his haughty pride
    To hear them laugh around.

'Come thou, Sir Tristram,' quoth the King.
    Quoth he, 'It cannot be,
For ne'er can I my stomach bring
    To do it willingly.'

'Wilt thou, Sir Kay, thou scornful wight?'
    Quoth Kay, 'Nay, by my troth!
What noble dame would kiss a knight
    That kissed so foul a mouth?'

'Wilt thou, Gawaine?' 'I cannot, King.'
    'Sir Geraint?' 'Nay, not I;
My kisses no relief could bring,
    For sooner would I die.'

Then up and spake the youngest man
    Of all about the board,
'Now such relief as Christian can
    I'll give to her, my lord.'

It was Sir Keith, a youthful knight,
    Yet strong of limb and bold,
With beard upon his chin as light
    As finest threads of gold.

Quoth Kay, 'He hath no mistress yet
    That he may call his own,
But here is one that's quick to get,
    As she herself has shown.'

He kissed her once, he kissed her twice,
    He kissed her three times o'er,
A wondrous change came in a trice,
    And she was foul no more.

Her cheeks grew red as any rose,
    Her brow as white as lawn,
Her bosom like the winter snows,
    Her eyes like those of fawn.

Her breath grew sweet as summer breeze
    That blows the meadows o'er;
Her voice grew soft as rustling trees,
    And cracked and harsh no more.

Her hair grew glittering, like the gold,
    Her hands as white as milk;
Her filthy rags, so foul and old,
    Were changed to robes of silk.

In great amaze the knights did stare.
    Quoth Kay, 'I make my vow
If it will please thee, lady fair,
    I'll gladly kiss thee now.'

But young Sir Keith kneeled on one knee
    And kissed her robes so fair.
'O let me be thy slave,' said he,
    'For none to thee compare.'

She bent her down, she kissed his brow,
    She kissed his lips and eyes.
Quoth she, 'Thou art my master now,
    My lord, my love, arise!

'And all the wealth that is mine own,
    My lands, I give to thee,
For never knight hath lady shown
    Such noble courtesy.

'Bewitched was I, in bitter pain,
    But thou hast set me free,
So now I am myself again,
    I give myself to thee.'

COPYBOOK: Copy select parts of the poem in the space below. Use the box on the previous page to illustrate the poem.

_____

_____

_____

_____

_____

_____

_____

_____

_____

_____

_____

_____

_____

_____

_____

_____

_____

_____

_____

_____

_____

_____

_____

_____

_____

_____

_____

_____

_____

VOCABULARY:

lordling	used here to mean a young lord; often a lord or nobleman of low rank
eave	the overhanging edge of a roof
helm	shortened form of "helmet"
greave	armor that covers the shin
dame	elderly woman
nigh	near; close to
bleared	blurred from swelling or tears
lank	stringy and limp
boon	a request or petition
gnaw	eat at; constantly worry
smart	sharp pain
childe	youth of noble birth
ween	expect; think or hope
wight	any living thing; usually refers to a human being
chivalry	the moral code of knight, rooted in Christian values
haughty	having an attitude of superiority and contempt for others
troth	truth; a promise
trice	instant
lawn	a thin cloth typically made of linen
bewitched	controlled or altered by magic or witchcraft; spellbound

ANALYZE:

1. Think about the rhyming pattern of this poem. What is the rhyme scheme? _____

    _____

2. How does the rhyme scheme and the meter affect the tone and mood of the poem as a whole?

    _____

    _____

    _____

    _____

COMPREHENSION QUESTIONS:

1. What does the woman want from King Arthur and his knights and why does she ask for this?_____

    _____

    _____

    _____

2. What are the two conditions which the dame gives the knights for her request?_____

    _____

    _____

    _____

3. How do the knights react to her request? Are they willing to help? Why or why not? _____

    _____

    _____

    _____

4. Who volunteers to help her? What is the result? _____

    _____

    _____

    _____

5. What is one moral lesson to be taken from this poem? _____

    _____

    _____

    _____

    _____

    _____

    _____

    _____

THE BRAVE OLD OAK
Henry Fothergill Chorley

A song to the oak, the brave old oak,
Who hath ruled in the greenwood long;
Here's health and renown to his broad green crown,
And his fifty arms so strong.
There's fear in his frown when the sun goes down,
And the fire in the west fades out;
And he showeth his might on a wild midnight,
When the storms through his branches shout.

Then here's to the oak, the brave old oak,
Who stands in his pride alone;
And still flourish he, a hale green tree,
When a hundred years are gone!

In the days of old, when the spring with cold
Had brightened his branches gray,
Through the grass at his feet crept maidens sweet,
To gather the dew of May.
And on that day to the rebeck gay
They frolicked with lovesome swains;
They are gone, they are dead, in the churchyard laid,
But the tree it still remains.

Then here's to the oak, the brave old oak,
Who stands in his pride alone;
And still flourish he, a hale green tree,
When a hundred years are gone!

He saw the rare times when the Christmas chimes
Were a merry sound to hear,
When the squire's wide hall and the cottage small
Were filled with good English cheer.
Now gold hath sway we all obey,
And a ruthless king is he;
But he never shall send our ancient friend
To be tossed on the stormy sea.

Then here's to the oak, the brave old oak,
Who stands in his pride alone;
And still flourish he, a hale green tree,
When a hundred years are gone!

COPYBOOK: Copy the poem in the space below. Use the box on the previous page to illustrate the poem.

VOCABULARY:

flourish   to prosper; to grow

rebeck   a medieval string instrument

swain   a male admirer, usually a peasant or country lad

ruthless   without pity or compassion; cruel

ANALYZE:

1. Think about the rhyming structure of this poem. Write out the rhyme scheme for each stanza. Are they identical? _____

    _____

    _____

    _____

2. What is the refrain of this poem? Think about the overall structure of the poem. What does it remind you of? What else could you call the refrain? _____

    _____

    _____

    _____

COMPREHENSION QUESTIONS:

1. The speaker uses metaphors as description throughout the first stanza instead of explaining directly. Give the intended meaning for the following:
    a. fifty arms — _____
    b. fire in the west — _____
    c. broad green crown — _____
    d. frown — _____

2. Why do you think the author chose to use metaphors for the tree's description instead of direct description? What do metaphors accomplish that could not be accomplished with direct description?

    _____

    _____

    _____

    _____

    _____

3. The author of this poem is able to convey a lot of meaning with few words. Analyze the line, "Who stands in his pride alone." Think about each word and how it contributes to the overall meaning of the line. What literary devices are used? _____

_____

_____

_____

_____

4. Often in poetry, words are chosen that can have (and do have) multiple meanings. In the line "Who stands in his pride alone," the nuances of the definition of the word "stand" can alter how you interpret the line. Give synonyms for "stand," and consider how replacing it with the new word or phrase in the poem changes the meaning of the line. _____

_____

_____

_____

5. In the third stanza the speaker uses the words "we" and "our." What effect does this have on you as a reader?

_____

_____

_____

6. What is meant by the line, "To be tossed on the stormy sea"? _____

_____

_____

_____

7. Compare a world where "gold hath sway we all obey" to the merry old England from the "days of old.

_____

_____

_____

8. What kind of symbolism is associated with oak trees? _____

_____

_____

_____

COLUMBUS
Joaquin Miller

Behind him lay the gray Azores,
  Behind the Gates of Hercules;
Before him not the ghost of shores,
  Before him only shoreless seas.
The good mate said: "Now must we pray,
  For lo! the very stars are gone.
Brave Admiral, speak, what shall I say?"
  "Why, say, 'Sail on! sail on! and on!'"

"My men grow mutinous day by day;
  My men grow ghastly wan and weak."
The stout mate thought of home; a spray
  Of salt wave washed his swarthy cheek.
"What shall I say, brave Admiral, say,
  If we sight naught but seas at dawn?"
"Why, you shall say at break of day,
  'Sail on! sail on! sail on! and on!'"

They sailed and sailed, as winds might blow,
  Until at last the blanched mate said:
"Why, now not even God would know
  Should I and all my men fall dead.

These very winds forget their way,
  For God from these dread seas is gone.
Now speak, brave Admiral, speak and say."
  He said: "Sail on! sail on! and on!"

They sailed. They sailed. Then spake the mate:
  "This mad sea shows his teeth to-night.
He curls his lip, he lies in wait,
  With lifted teeth, as if to bite!
Brave Admiral, say but one good word:
  What shall we do when hope is gone?"
The words leapt like a leaping sword:
  "Sail on! sail on! sail on! and on!"

Then, pale and worn, he kept his deck,
  And peered through darkness. Ah, that night
Of all dark nights! And then a speck—
  A light! A light! A light! A light!
It grew, a starlit flag unfurled!
  It grew to be Time's burst of dawn.
He gained a world; he gave that world
  Its grandest lesson: "On! sail on!"

COPYBOOK: Copy the poem in the space below. Use the box on the previous page to illustrate the poem.

VOCABULARY:

Azores	a group of islands in the Atlantic
mutinous	rebellious, uncontrollable
wan	unnaturally pale
swarthy	having a dark complexion or color
Gates of Hercules	high points on the south of Spain (Gibraltar) and northwest Africa
naught	nothing
blanched	turned white or became pale

ANALYZE:

1. Think about the rhyming structure of this poem. Label each line and then write out the rhyme scheme.

   _____

2. What is the refrain of this poem? _____

3. Aside from the narrator, there are two main speakers in this poem, the mate and the Admiral. Underline the Admiral's quotations.

1   Behind him lay the gray Azores, _____
2   Behind the Gates of Hercules; _____
3   Before him not the ghost of shores, _____
4   Before him only shoreless seas. _____
5   The good mate said: "Now must we pray, _____
6   For lo! the very stars are gone. _____
7   Brave Admiral, speak, what shall I say?" _____
8   "Why, say, 'Sail on! sail on! and on!'" _____

9   "My men grow mutinous day by day; _____
10   My men grow ghastly wan and weak." _____
11 The stout mate thought of home; a spray _____
12   Of salt wave washed his swarthy cheek. _____
13 "What shall I say, brave Admiral, say, _____
14   If we sight naught but seas at dawn?" _____
15 "Why, you shall say at break of day, _____
16   'Sail on! sail on! sail on! and on!'" _____

17 They sailed and sailed, as winds might blow, _____
18   Until at last the blanched mate said: _____
19 "Why, now not even God would know _____
20   Should I and all my men fall dead. _____

21 These very winds forget their way, _____
22   For God from these dread seas is gone. _____
23 Now speak, brave Admiral, speak and say." _____
24   He said: "Sail on! sail on! and on!" _____

25 They sailed. They sailed. Then spake the mate: ___
26   "This mad sea shows his teeth to-night. _____
27 He curls his lip, he lies in wait, _____
28   With lifted teeth, as if to bite! _____
29 Brave Admiral, say but one good word: _____
30   What shall we do when hope is gone?" _____
31 The words leapt like a leaping sword: _____
32   "Sail on! sail on! sail on! and on!" _____

33 Then, pale and worn, he kept his deck, _____
34   And peered through darkness. Ah, that night ___
35 Of all dark nights! And then a speck— _____
36   A light! A light! A light! A light! _____
37 It grew, a starlit flag unfurled! _____
38   It grew to be Time's burst of dawn. _____
39 He gained a world; he gave that world _____
40   Its grandest lesson: "On! sail on!" _____

COMPREHENSION QUESTIONS:

1. Who was Christopher Columbus? When did he make his famous voyage to the Americas? _____

_____

_____

2. What was the purpose of his journey? _____

_____

_____

3. Why would the speaker make reference to the Azores and the Gates of Hercules? _____

_____

_____

4. In each of the first four stanzas, Columbus and his crew meet with a challenge. Name the challenge in

   each stanza.

_____

_____

5. Why was the good mate alarmed when they could not see the stars? _____

_____

_____

6. Why might the crew have grown mutinous? _____

_____

_____

7. What does the good mate mean when he says, "not even God would know should I and all my men

   fall dead"? _____

_____

_____

8. Why would the good mate be alarmed by the lack of wind in the third stanza? _____

_____

_____

9. What is personified in the fourth stanza? What is the crew experiencing? _____

_____

_____

10. Explain the simile in line 31. _____

_____

_____

_____

11. What response do you think the good mate hopes to hear from the Admiral each time they face a

challenge? How does the good mate respond to the Admiral's commands? _____

_____

_____

_____

12. What could "a light!" represent in the last stanza? What about "a starlit flag unfurled," or "Time's burst

of dawn"? _____

_____

_____

_____

13. What is the world's grandest lesson? _____

_____

_____

_____

14. Columbus faces great adversity on his journey, but does not relent. How do you decide whether it is

worthwhile to continue and when it is wise to turn back and think of another strategy?_____

_____

_____

_____

_____

_____

PAUL REVERE'S RIDE
Henry Wadsworth Longfellow

1 Listen, my children, and you shall hear
2 Of the midnight ride of Paul Revere,
3 On the eighteenth of April, in Seventy-five;
4 Hardly a man is now alive
5 Who remembers that famous day and year.

6 He said to his friend, "If the British march
7 By land or sea from the town to-night,
8 Hang a lantern aloft in the belfry arch
9 Of the North Church tower as a signal light,—
10 One if by land, and two, if by sea;
11 And I on the opposite shore will be,
12 Ready to ride and spread the alarm
13 Through every Middlesex village and farm,
14 For the country folk to be up and to arm."

15 Then he said "Good-night!" and with muffled oar
16 Silently rowed to the Charlestown shore,
17 Just as the moon rose over the bay,
18 Where swinging wide at her moorings lay
19 The Somerset, British man-of-war;
20 A phantom ship, with each mast and spar
21 Across the moon like a prison bar,
22 And a huge black hulk, that was magnified
23 By its own reflection in the tide.

24 Meanwhile, his friend through alley and street,
25 Wanders and watches with eager ears,
26 Till in the silence around him he hears
27 The muster of men at the barrack door,
28 The sound of arms, and the tramp of feet,
29 And the measured tread of the grenadiers,
30 Marching down to their boats on the shore.

31 Then he climbed the tower of the Old
    North Church
32 By the wooden stairs, with stealthy tread,
33 To the belfry chamber overhead,
34 And startled the pigeons from their perch
35 On the sombre rafters, that round him made
36 Masses and moving shapes of shade,—
37 By the trembling ladder, steep and tall,
38 To the highest window in the wall,
39 Where he paused to listen and look down
40 A moment on the roofs of the town
41 And the moonlight flowing over all.
42 Beneath, in the churchyard, lay the dead,

43 In their night encampment on the hill,
44 Wrapped in silence so deep and still
45 That he could hear, like a sentinel's tread,
46 The watchful night-wind, as it went
47 Creeping along from tent to tent,
48 And seeming to whisper, "All is well!"
49 A moment only he feels the spell
50 Of the place and the hour, and the secret dread
51 Of the lonely belfry and the dead;
52 For suddenly all his thoughts are bent
53 On a shadowy something far away,
54 Where the river widens to meet the bay,—
55 A line of black that bends and floats
56 On the rising tide like a bridge of boats.

57 Meanwhile, impatient to mount and ride,
58 Booted and spurred, with a heavy stride
59 On the opposite shore walked Paul Revere.
60 Now he patted his horse's side,
61 Now he gazed at the landscape far and near,
62 Then, impetuous, stamped the earth,
63 And turned and tightened his saddle girth;
64 But mostly he watched with eager search
65 The belfry tower of the Old North Church,
66 As it rose above the graves on the hill,
67 Lonely and spectral and sombre and still.
68 And lo! as he looks, on the belfry's height
69 A glimmer, and then a gleam of light!
70 He springs to the saddle, the bridle he turns,
71 But lingers and gazes, till full on his sight
72 A second lamp in the belfry burns.

73 A hurry of hoofs in a village street,
74 A shape in the moonlight, a bulk in the dark,
75 And beneath, from the pebbles, in passing,
    a spark
76 Struck out by a steed flying fearless and fleet;
77 That was all! And yet, through the gloom and
    the light,
78 The fate of a nation was riding that night;
79 And the spark struck out by that steed, in
    his flight,
80 Kindled the land into flame with its heat.
81 He has left the village and mounted the steep,
82 And beneath him, tranquil and broad and deep,
83 Is the Mystic, meeting the ocean tides;
84 And under the alders that skirt its edge,

85 Now soft on the sand, now loud on the ledge,
86 Is heard the tramp of his steed as he rides.

87 It was twelve by the village clock
88 When he crossed the bridge into Medford town.
89 He heard the crowing of the cock,
90 And the barking of the farmer's dog,
91 And felt the damp of the river fog,
92 That rises after the sun goes down.

93 It was one by the village clock,
94 When he galloped into Lexington.
95 He saw the gilded weathercock
96 Swim in the moonlight as he passed,
97 And the meeting-house windows, black
   and bare,
98 Gaze at him with a spectral glare,
99 As if they already stood aghast
100 At the bloody work they would look upon.

101 It was two by the village clock,
102 When he came to the bridge in Concord town.
103 He heard the bleating of the flock,
104 And the twitter of birds among the trees,
105 And felt the breath of the morning breeze
106 Blowing over the meadow brown.

107 And one was safe and asleep in his bed
108 Who at the bridge would be first to fall,
109 Who that day would be lying dead,
110 Pierced by a British musket ball.

111 You know the rest. In the books you have read
112 How the British Regulars fired and fled,—
113 How the farmers gave them ball for ball,
114 From behind each fence and farmyard wall,
115 Chasing the redcoats down the lane,
116 Then crossing the fields to emerge again
117 Under the trees at the turn of the road,
118 And only pausing to fire and load.

119 So through the night rode Paul Revere;
120 And so through the night went his cry of alarm
121 To every Middlesex village and farm,—
122 A cry of defiance, and not of fear,
123 A voice in the darkness, a knock at the door,
124 And a word that shall echo for evermore!
125 For, borne on the night-wind of the Past,
126 Through all our history, to the last,
127 In the hour of darkness and peril and need,
128 The people will waken and listen to hear
129 The hurrying hoof-beats of that steed,
130 And the midnight message of Paul Revere.

ANALYZE:

1. Think about the rhyming structure of this poem. Is there a regular or repeated rhyme scheme?

   _____

   _____

2. Underline the names of significant historical places in the poem.

3. Summarize the story of the poem in your own words. _____

   _____

   _____

   _____

   _____

   _____

   _____

   _____

COMPREHENSION QUESTIONS:

1. This poem is based on a historical event. Read "The History of Paul Revere's Ride" in the Appendix. What are possible reasons for the discrepancies between the historical event and Longfellow's poem?

_____

_____

2. What simile is used to describe the *Somerset* in lines 20-23? Why do you think the author chose this image?

_____

_____

3. In lines 73-80, Revere's steed sets off a spark that kindles "the land into flame with its head." What does this mean? _____

_____

_____

4. There are several examples of personification in this poem. Find them and discuss how they contribute to the poem's narrative. _____

_____

_____

_____

5. We see the progression of time and space in lines 87-110. As Revere travels farther, what happens to the tone of the poem? _____

_____

_____

_____

6. Longfellow wrote this poem a few months before the Civil War began. In this historical context, what "message" (line 130) do you think he might be trying to convey to his audience?_____

_____

_____

_____

_____

_____

_____

COPYBOOK: Copy the poem in the space below. Use the box on the previous page to illustrate the poem.

O CAPTAIN! MY CAPTAIN!
Walt Whitman

O Captain! my Captain! our fearful trip is done;
The ship has weather'd every rack, the prize we sought is won;
The port is near, the bells I hear, the people all exulting,
While follow eyes the steady keel, the vessel grim and daring:
    But O heart! heart! heart!
    O the bleeding drops of red,
    Where on the deck my Captain lies,
      Fallen cold and dead.

O Captain! my Captain! rise up and hear the bells;
Rise up—for you the flag is flung—for you the bugle trills;
For you bouquets and ribbon'd wreaths—for you the shores a-crowding;
For you they call, the swaying mass, their eager faces turning;
    Here Captain! dear father!
    This arm beneath your head;
    It is some dream that on the deck,
      You've fallen cold and dead.

My Captain does not answer, his lips are pale and still;
My father does not feel my arm, he has no pulse nor will;
The ship is anchor'd safe and sound, its voyage closed and done;
From fearful trip, the victor ship, comes in with object won;
    Exult, O shores, and ring, O bells!
    But I, with mournful tread,
    Walk the deck my Captain lies,
      Fallen cold and dead.

COPYBOOK: Copy the poem in the space below. Use the box on the previous page to illustrate the poem.

VOCABULARY:

keel   the main structural part of a ship that the rest of the ship is built around, helps give the ship stability in the water

grim   somber; without joy

mournful   sad; heavy; sorrowful; grieving the dead

ANALYZE:

1. Background: This poem is an elegy. President Abraham Lincoln was assassinated five days after the official end of the Civil War. Walt Whitman was a great admirer of Lincoln, and wrote this poem to honor his memory and express the national grief at his death. Knowing this historical context, reread the poem.

2. What figure of speech is employed throughout the poem to compare the events described in the poem to the historical events that inspired it? _____

3. Think about the rhyming structure of the poem. Is there a set rhyme scheme? _____

    _____

    _____

COMPREHENSION QUESTIONS:

1. If we read the poem as an elegy for Abraham Lincoln, the people, places, and things in the poem can symbolize something other than their obvious meaning in the poem. What could the following things symbolize?

A. captain/father _____

B. ship_____

C. prize_____

D. fearful trip_____

E. people cheering the ship_____

F. port_____

2. The format of the poem is deliberate. How does the format affect the way you read the poem? Is there a difference in tone or content between the long lines and the short lines? _____

   _____

   _____

   _____

   _____

   _____

3. Whom is the speaker addressing in the poem? Does it change? _____

   _____

   _____

   _____

   _____

   _____

   _____

4. In what ways could you interpret the word "heart" in line 5? To whose heart is it referring? _____

   _____

   _____

   _____

   _____

   _____

THE DWARVES' SONG
J. R. R. Tolkien

COPYBOOK: Copy "The Dwarves' Song" from Chapter 1 of *The Hobbit*. It begins "Far over the misty mountains cold …." Use the box on page 120 to illustrate the poem.

VOCABULARY:

yore	times past; history; of old
fell	high, barren field; moor
hoard	vast collection, usually guarded jealously
wrought	made; shaped; formed
meshed	combined; fused together
dale	wide valley
ire	wrath; vengeful anger

ANALYZE:

1. Think about the rhyming structure of this poem. Write out the rhyme scheme. _____

   _____

2. In addition to the end line rhyme scheme, what other rhyming pattern occurs in this poem?_____

   _____

3. What is the refrain of this poem? _____

   _____

   _____

COMPREHENSION QUESTIONS:

1. Summarize the story the speaker tells in the poem. _____

   _____

   _____

   _____

   _____

   _____

2. Why does the refrain change slightly in the last stanza?_____

   _____

   _____

   _____

3. What is the "tramp of doom"? _____

   _____

   _____

   _____

4. Identify and explain an example of personification from the poem._____

   _____

   _____

   _____

   _____

5. Identify and explain an example of simile from the poem. _____

   _____

   _____

   _____

   _____

6. Is the poem told in present or past tense? Is it the same throughout the poem?_____

   _____

   _____

   _____

   _____

THE LADY OF SHALOTT
Alfred, Lord Tennyson

Part I
On either side the river lie
Long fields of barley and of rye,
That clothe the wold and meet the sky;
And through the field the road runs by
5   To many-towered Camelot;
And up and down the people go,
Gazing where the lilies blow
Round an island there below,
      The island of Shalott.

10 Willows whiten, aspens quiver,
Little breezes dusk and shiver
Through the wave that runs for ever
By the island in the river
      Flowing down to Camelot.
15 Four grey walls, and four grey towers,
Overlook a space of flowers,
And the silent isle imbowers
      The Lady of Shalott.

By the margin, willow-veiled,
20 Slide the heavy barges trailed
By slow horses; and unhailed
The shallop flitteth silken-sailed
      Skimming down to Camelot:
But who hath seen her wave her hand?
25 Or at the casement seen her stand?
Or is she known in all the land,
      The Lady of Shalott?

Only reapers, reaping early
In among the bearded barley,
30 Hear a song that echoes cheerly
From the river winding clearly,
      Down to towered Camelot:
And by the moon the reaper weary,
Piling sheaves in uplands airy,
35 Listening, whispers, "'Tis the fairy
      Lady of Shalott."

Part II
There she weaves by night and day
A magic web with colours gay.
She has heard a whisper say,
40 A curse is on her if she stay
      To look down to Camelot.

She knows not what the curse may be,
And so she weaveth steadily,
And little other care hath she,
45   The Lady of Shalott.

And moving through a mirror clear
That hangs before her all the year,
Shadows of the world appear.
There she sees the highway near
50   Winding down to Camelot:
There the river eddy whirls,
And there the surly village-churls,
And the red cloaks of market girls,
      Pass onward from Shalott.

55 Sometimes a troop of damsels glad,
An abbot on an ambling pad,
Sometimes a curly shepherd-lad,
Or long-haired page in crimson clad,
      Goes by to towered Camelot;
60 And sometimes through the mirror blue
The knights come riding two and two:
She hath no loyal knight and true,
      The Lady of Shalott.

But in her web she still delights
65 To weave the mirror's magic sights,
For often through the silent nights
A funeral, with plumes and lights
      And music, went to Camelot:
Or when the moon was overhead,
70 Came two young lovers lately wed;
"I am half sick of shadows," said
      The Lady of Shalott.

Part III
A bow-shot from her bower-eaves,
He rode between the barley-sheaves,
75 The sun came dazzling through the leaves,
And flamed upon the brazen greaves
      Of bold Sir Lancelot.
A red-cross knight for ever kneeled
To a lady in his shield,
80 That sparkled on the yellow field,
      Beside remote Shalott.

The gemmy bridle glittered free,
Like to some branch of stars we see
Hung in the golden Galaxy.
85 The bridle bells rang merrily
　　　As he rode down to Camelot:
And from his blazoned baldric slung
A mighty silver bugle hung,
And as he rode his armour rung,
90　　　Beside remote Shalott.

All in the blue unclouded weather
Thick-jewelled shone the saddle-leather,
The helmet and the helmet-feather
Burned like one burning flame together,
95　　　As he rode down to Camelot.
As often through the purple night,
Below the starry clusters bright,
Some bearded meteor, trailing light,
　　　Moves over still Shalott.

100 His broad clear brow in sunlight glowed;
On burnished hooves his war-horse trode;
From underneath his helmet flowed
His coal-black curls as on he rode,
　　　As he rode down to Camelot.
105 From the bank and from the river
He flashed into the crystal mirror,
"Tirra lirra," by the river
　　　Sang Sir Lancelot.

She left the web, she left the loom,
110 She made three paces through the room,
She saw the water-lily bloom,
She saw the helmet and the plume,
　　　She looked down to Camelot.
Out flew the web and floated wide;
115 The mirror cracked from side to side;
"The curse is come upon me," cried
　　　The Lady of Shalott.

Part IV
In the stormy east-wind straining,
The pale yellow woods were waning,
120 The broad stream in his banks complaining,
Heavily the low sky raining
　　　Over towered Camelot;
Down she came and found a boat
Beneath a willow left afloat,
125 And round about the prow she wrote
　　　The Lady of Shalott.

And down the river's dim expanse,
Like some bold seër in a trance
Seeing all his own mischance—
130 With a glassy countenance
　　　Did she look to Camelot.
And at the closing of the day
She loosed the chain, and down she lay;
The broad stream bore her far away,
135　　　The Lady of Shalott.

Lying, robed in snowy white
That loosely flew to left and right—
The leaves upon her falling light—
Through the noises of the night
140　　　She floated down to Camelot:
And as the boat-head wound along
The willowy hills and fields among,
They heard her singing her last song,
　　　The Lady of Shalott.

145 Heard a carol, mournful, holy,
Chanted loudly, chanted lowly,
Till her blood was frozen slowly,
And her eyes were darkened wholly,
　　　Turned to towered Camelot.
150 For ere she reached upon the tide
The first house by the water-side,
Singing in her song she died,
　　　The Lady of Shalott.

Under tower and balcony,
155 By garden-wall and gallery,
A gleaming shape she floated by,
Dead-pale between the houses high,
　　　Silent into Camelot.
Out upon the wharfs they came,
160 Knight and burgher, lord and dame,
And round the prow they read her name,
　　　The Lady of Shalott.

Who is this? and what is here?
And in the lighted palace near
165 Died the sound of royal cheer;
And they crossed themselves for fear,
　　　All the knights at Camelot:
But Lancelot mused a little space;
He said, "She has a lovely face;
170 God in his mercy lend her grace,
　　　The Lady of Shalott."

COPYBOOK: Copy your favorite parts of the poem below. Use the box on the previous page to illustrate the poem.

VOCABULARY:

imbowers	shelters or encloses in
shallop	a small open boat
casement	a window with sashes that open
surly	ill-humored; gruff
churl	a medieval English peasant
greaves	leg armor worn below the knees
gemmy	full of, or set with, gems
baldric	a belt worn across the chest to support a sword or bugle
loom	an apparatus for making thread into cloth by weaving strands together
prow	the front end of a ship
countenance	the expression of the face
burgher	a citizen of a city

ANALYZE:

1. Think about the rhyming structure of this poem. Write out the rhyme scheme. _____

_____

2. What are the two refrains in this poem? Are they always exactly the same?_____

_____

_____

3. Summarize the story of the poem in your own words. _____

_____

_____

_____

_____

_____

_____

_____

_____

_____

_____

_____

COMPREHENSION QUESTIONS:

PART I

1. Describe the setting. _____
   _____
   _____

2. What is the imagery in lines 10-12? _____
   _____
   _____

3. What is on the island? Who lives there? _____
   _____
   _____

4. What is the "margin"? What goes by, and where do they go?_____
   _____
   _____

5. Does anyone ever see the Lady of Shalott? How do they know she is there? _____
   _____
   _____

6. What do the reapers call her? Why do you think they would call her that? _____
   _____
   _____

PART II

7. What is her occupation? _____
   _____
   _____

8. What is the curse? Does the poem tell who whispered the curse or what it really means?_____
   _____
   _____

9. How does she feel about the curse? Is she concerned about breaking it?_____
   _____
   _____

10. How does she see the world outside her tower? _____

_____

11. What indicators do we have by the end of Part II that she is not quite content with her life? _____

_____

_____

12. What are the people outside moving toward? Give words that describe the movement. _____

_____

13. What does the Lady of Shalott move toward? _____

_____

14. How does the Lady of Shalott feel about weaving at the beginning of Part II? At the end? _____

_____

15. What does the Lady mean by saying, "I am half sick of shadows"? _____

_____

_____

PART III

16. Who comes riding "between the barley-sheaves"? How is he described? _____

_____

17. With what sort of imagery is Lancelot repeatedly associated? Give examples. _____

_____

_____

18. What could this imagery be suggesting about Lancelot? _____

_____

_____

_____

19. Describe Sir Lancelot's appearance. _____

_____

_____

_____

20. What is the simile in lines 82-84? _____

_____

_____

21. To what is Lancelot's appearance compared?_____

_____

_____

22. How does Lancelot flash into the mirror? _____

_____

_____

23. In lines 109-113, what is the effect of the repetition of "she"? Why do you think this repetition is used?

_____

_____

24. How and why does the curse come upon her?_____

_____

_____

_____

25. What does the Lady see when she finally looks out the window?_____

_____

_____

26. What happens to the web and mirror when the curse comes upon her? ___

_____

_____

27. How does the weather affect the mood of lines 118-122? _____

_____

_____

_____

28. Why do you think she finds a boat and writes her name on it? _____

_____

_____

29. What is the Lady compared to in lines 127-131? _____

_____

_____

30. What is the Lady's mood as she prepares her boat and sets off? _____

_____

_____

_____

31. At what time of day does she leave for Camelot? _____

_____

_____

32. What is she wearing? What could the significance of this be? _____

_____

_____

_____

33. Why might she travel at night? _____

_____

_____

34. Why is she singing her last song? What is it like? _____

_____

_____

35. At what point do you realize that the consequence of breaking the curse is death? What are some clues?

_____

_____

_____

36. Describe the death of the Lady of Shalott. _____

_____

_____

37. Describe what sights the boat passes as it enters Camelot. What is the mood?_____

_____

_____

_____

38. Describe the Lady's appearance as she floats down the river. _____

_____

_____

39. Does Lancelot know who she is? _____

_____

_____

_____

40. There are two motifs that run through the poem, one associated with the Lady of Shalott and one with

Lancelot. Imagery associated with these characters is often pulled from these motifs. What are they?

Give examples from throughout the poem, and explain how this imagery deepens our understanding of

each character. _____

_____

_____

_____

_____

_____

_____

_____

_____

_____

_____

_____

_____

_____

_____

_____

THE BELLS
Edgar Allan Poe

I.

Hear the sledges with the bells—
　　Silver bells!
What a world of merriment their melody foretells!
　　How they tinkle, tinkle, tinkle,
　　　In the icy air of night!
　　While the stars that oversprinkle
　　All the heavens, seem to twinkle
　　　With a crystalline delight;
　　Keeping time, time, time,
　　In a sort of Runic rhyme,
To the tintinnabulation that so musically wells
　From the bells, bells, bells, bells,
　　　Bells, bells, bells—
From the jingling and the tinkling of the bells.

II.

　　Hear the mellow wedding bells
　　　Golden bells!
What a world of happiness their harmony foretells!
　　Through the balmy air of night
　　How they ring out their delight!
　　　From the molten-golden notes,
　　　　And all in tune,
　　　What a liquid ditty floats
　To the turtle-dove that listens, while she gloats
　　　On the moon!
　　Oh, from out the sounding cells,
What a gush of euphony voluminously wells!
　　　How it swells!
　　　How it dwells
　　On the Future! how it tells
　　Of the rapture that impels
　　To the swinging and the ringing
　　Of the bells, bells, bells,
　Of the bells, bells, bells, bells,
　　　Bells, bells, bells—
To the rhyming and the chiming of the bells!

III.

　　Hear the loud alarum bells—
　　　Brazen bells!
What tale of terror, now, their turbulency tells!
　　In the startled ear of night

How they scream out their affright!
　　Too much horrified to speak,
　　They can only shriek, shriek,
　　　　Out of tune,
In a clamorous appealing to the mercy of the fire,
In a mad expostulation with the deaf and frantic fire,
　　　Leaping higher, higher, higher,
　　　With a desperate desire,
　　And a resolute endeavor
　　Now—now to sit or never,
　By the side of the pale-faced moon.
　　　Oh, the bells, bells, bells!
　　　What a tale their terror tells
　　　　Of Despair!
　How they clang, and clash, and roar!
　What a horror they outpour
On the bosom of the palpitating air!
　　Yet the ear, it fully knows,
　　　By the twanging,
　　　And the clanging,
　　How the danger ebbs and flows;
　　Yet, the ear distinctly tells,
　　　In the jangling,
　　　And the wrangling,
　　How the danger sinks and swells,
By the sinking or the swelling in the anger of the bells—
　　　Of the bells—
　Of the bells, bells, bells, bells,
　　Bells, bells, bells—
In the clamour and the clangour of the bells!

IV.
　　Hear the tolling of the bells—
　　　Iron bells!
What a world of solemn thought their monody compels!
　　In the silence of the night,
　　How we shiver with affright
　At the melancholy meaning of their tone!
　　For every sound that floats
　　From the rust within their throats
　　　Is a groan.
　　And the people—ah, the people—
　　They that dwell up in the steeple,
　　　All alone,
　　And who, tolling, tolling, tolling,
　　　In that muffled monotone,
　　Feel a glory in so rolling
　　　On the human heart a stone—

They are neither man nor woman—
They are neither brute nor human—
    They are Ghouls:—
  And their king it is who tolls;
  And he rolls, rolls, rolls, rolls,
     Rolls
    A pæan from the bells!
  And his merry bosom swells
    With the pæan of the bells!
  And he dances, and he yells;
Keeping time, time, time,
In a sort of Runic rhyme,
    To the pæan of the bells—
     Of the bells:
Keeping time, time, time,
In a sort of Runic rhyme,
    To the throbbing of the bells—
   Of the bells, bells, bells—
    To the sobbing of the bells;
Keeping time, time, time,
   As he knells, knells, knells,
In a happy Runic rhyme,
    To the rolling of the bells—
  Of the bells, bells, bells—
    To the tolling of the bells,
Of the bells, bells, bells, bells—
    Bells, bells, bells—
To the moaning and the groaning of the bells.

COPYBOOK: Copy your favorite parts of the poem below. Use the box on the previous page to illustrate the poem.

VOCABULARY:

sledge	a heavy sled
crystalline	clear and sparkling
tintinnabulation	the sound of ringing bells
balmy	(of weather) mild and pleasant
gloat	to delight in a victory with smug satisfaction
euphony	a pleasing sound; a harmonious succession of words
voluminous	of great volume or size
alarum	alarm
brazen	made of brass; bold and shameless
turbulency	violent agitation
clamour	continuous loud noise
expostulation	an act of earnestly reasoning with someone against something they are doing
resolute	determined; firm in purpose
clangour	medley of *clangs*; loud continuous noise
monody	music made by one voice or instrument; often an elegy or dirge
melancholy	gloomy; somber; mournful
pæan	a song of praise or joy or victory
knell	(v.) to make a mournful sound (n.) the sound made by a funeral bell; the sound announcing a death

ANALYZE:

1. There are many instances of personification throughout the poem. Read through the poem again and underline them. Name four objects or entities that are personified. _____

   _____

   _____

COMPREHENSION QUESTIONS:

1. The speaker refers to a different type of bell in each stanza. What are they? What is the purpose of each?

   _____

   _____

   _____

   _____

   _____

   _____

2. Who is the audience of the poem? Whom is the speaker addressing? _____

_____

_____

_____

3. The events in each stanza all take place at night, but the stanzas have very different tones. What is the mood of each stanza? What specific words and images does the author use to create each mood?

_____

_____

_____

_____

_____

_____

_____

_____

_____

_____

_____

4. How do alliteration, assonance, and onomatopoeia contribute to the mood of each stanza? Give specific examples.

_____

_____

_____

_____

_____

_____

_____

_____

_____

_____

TREES
Joyce Kilmer

I think that I shall never see
A poem as lovely as a tree.

A tree whose hungry mouth is prest
Against the sweet earth's flowing breast;

A tree who looks at God all day,
And lifts her leafy arms to pray;

A tree who may in summer wear
A nest of robins in her hair;

Upon whose bosom snow has lain;
Who intimately lives with rain.

Poems are made by fools like me,
But only God can make a tree.

COPYBOOK: Copy the poem in the space below. Use the box on the previous page to illustrate the poem.

VOCABULARY:

intimately   closely; in a close manner

ANALYZE:

1. Think about the rhyming structure of this poem. Label each line and then write out the rhyme scheme.

    _____

2. What figure of speech is used throughout the poem to describe the tree?_____

    _____

1   I think that I shall never see   _____

2   A poem as lovely as a tree.   _____

3   A tree whose hungry mouth is prest   _____

4   Against the sweet earth's flowing breast;   _____

5   A tree who looks at God all day,   _____

6   And lifts her leafy arms to pray;   _____

7   A tree who may in summer wear   _____

8   A nest of robins in her hair;   _____

9   Upon whose bosom snow has lain;   _____

10 Who intimately lives with rain.   _____

11 Poems are made by fools like me,   _____

12 But only God can make a tree.   _____

COMPREHENSION QUESTIONS:

1. In this poem, do you think the author and the speaker can be assumed to be the same person? What

    evidence from the poem supports your answer? _____

    _____

    _____

    _____

    _____

2. What is the overall message the speaker is communicating? _____

    _____

    _____

    _____

    _____

3. What lesson can we take from the image of the tree in the third stanza? _____

    _____

    _____

    _____

    _____

I GO AMONG TREES

Wendell Berry

I go among trees and sit still.
All my stirring becomes quiet
around me like circles on water.
My tasks lie in their places
where I left them, asleep like cattle.

Then what is afraid of me comes
and lives a while in my sight.
What it fears in me leaves me,
and the fear of me leaves it.
It sings, and I hear its song.

Then what I am afraid of comes.
I live for a while in its sight.
What I fear in it leaves it,
and the fear of it leaves me.
It sings, and I hear its song.

After days of labor,
mute in my consternations,
I hear my song at last,
and I sing it. As we sing,
the day turns, the trees move.

COPYBOOK: Copy the poem in the space below. Use the box on the previous page to illustrate the poem.

VOCABULARY:

stirring   restlessness

consternation   a feeling of anxiety, dismay, dread, or confusion; alarm

ANALYZE:

1. Think about the rhyming structure of this poem. Is there a rhyme scheme? _____

   _____

2. Identify and explain the two similes in the first stanza. _____

   _____

   _____

   _____

COMPREHENSION QUESTIONS:

1. What is the mood of the first stanza? _____

   _____

2. Reread the second stanza. Think about what the speaker could mean by "what is afraid of me," "what it

   fears in me," and "I hear its song." Explain the stanza in your own words. _____

   _____

   _____

   _____

   _____

   _____

3. Reread the third stanza. Think about what the speaker could mean by "what I am afraid of," "I live for a

   while in its sight," and "I hear its song." Explain the stanza in your own words. _____

   _____

   _____

   _____

   _____

   _____

4. Reread the fourth stanza. Think about what the speaker could mean by "days of labor," "mute in my consternations," and "hear my song at last." _____

_____

_____

_____

_____

_____

_____

5. How are stanzas 2 and 3 different? How are they related to each other?_____

_____

_____

_____

6. Why do you think the fears come only after the speaker is still and quiet?_____

_____

_____

_____

7. According to the poem, what benefit is there in being "still"?_____

_____

_____

_____

8. Have you ever experienced a fear that seemed daunting, but that turned out to be manageable once you finally acknowledged and faced it? _____

_____

_____

_____

_____

IT IS NOT GROWING LIKE A TREE
Ben Jonson

It is not growing like a tree
In bulk, doth make Man better be;
Or standing long an oak, three hundred year,
To fall a log at last, dry, bald, and sere:
A lily of a day
Is fairer far in May,
Although it fall and die that night—
It was the plant and flower of Light.
In small proportions we just beauties see;
And in short measures life may perfect be.

COPYBOOK: Copy the poem in the space below. Use the box on the previous page to illustrate the poem.

VOCABULARY:

sere   dry; withered

bulk   size

proportions amounts

ANALYZE:

1. Think about the rhyming structure of this poem. Write out the rhyme scheme. _____

 _____

2. To what is man being compared in the opening lines? _____

 _____

 _____

 _____

3. To what is man being compared in the last half of the poem? _____

 _____

 _____

 _____

COMPREHENSION QUESTIONS:

1. What is the author saying about man striving to be like a tree? _____

    _____

    _____

    _____

    _____

2. What would it be better for a man to be like? Why? _____

    _____

    _____

    _____

    _____

3. What could the author mean by "the plant and flower of Light"? _____

    _____

    _____

    _____

    _____

4. What do you think the last lines mean? _____

    _____

    _____

    _____

    _____

    _____

    _____

    _____

PLANT A TREE
Lucy Larcom

He who plants a tree
Plants a hope.
Rootlets up through fibers blindly grope.
Leaves unfold into horizons free.
So man's life must climb
From the clods of time
Unto heavens sublime.
Canst thou prophesy, thou little tree,
What the glory of thy boughs shall be?

He who plants a tree
Plants a joy;
Plants a comfort that will never cloy;
Every day a fresh reality,
Beautiful and strong,
To whose shelter throng
Creatures blithe with song.
If thou couldst but know, thou happy tree,
Of the bliss that shall inhabit thee!

He who plants a tree,—
He plants peace.
Under its green curtains jargons cease.
Leaf and zephyr murmur soothingly;
Shadows soft with sleep
Down tired eyelids creep,
Balm of slumber deep.
Never hast thou dreamed, thou blessed tree,
Of the benediction thou shalt be.

He who plants a tree,—
He plants youth;
Vigor won for centuries in sooth;
Life of time, that hints eternity!
Boughs their strength uprear:
New shoots, every year
On old growths appear;
Thou shalt teach the ages, sturdy tree,
Youth of soul is immortality.

He who plants a tree,—
He plants love,
Tents of coolness spreading out above
Wayfarers he may not live to see.
Gifts that grow are best;
Hands that bless are blest;
Plant! life does the rest!
Heaven and earth help him who plants a tree,
And his work its own reward shall be.

COPYBOOK: Copy the poem in the space below. Use the box on the previous page to illustrate the poem.

VOCABULARY:

sublime	exalted; elevated; complete; imparting a sense of grandeur or awe
blithe	lighthearted and happy; carefree; cheerful
jargon	obscure, pretentious language; gibberish; unintelligible or meaningless words
zephyr	gentle breeze
benediction	a blessing; something that imparts blessings
vigor	healthy growth
uprear	to raise up; exalt
wayfarers	wanderers; travelers

ANALYZE:

1. Think about the rhyming structure of this poem. Write out the rhyme scheme. _____

   _____

2. What is the refrain of this poem? _____

   _____

3. What purpose does the refrain serve? _____

   _____

   _____

COMPREHENSION QUESTIONS:

1. In the first stanza, the author compares man's life to a newly planted tree. Explain the comparison.

2. Whom is the speaker addressing in the poem? Does it change? _____

3. Explain: "youth of soul is immortality." Do you agree? _____

APPENDIX

Glossary

Alliteration: the repetition of consonant sounds in consecutive or closely placed words
>Example: "**f**resh **f**ruits and **f**ine **f**lowers" (from "The Happy Farmer")

Often the alliterative sounds serve to emphasize the imagery of the lines. For example, in Charles Kingsley's "Ode to the Northeast Wind," in the line "**s**howers, **s**oft and **s**teaming," the repeated sounds of "s" imitate the sound of rain.

Apostrophe: a figure of speech wherein the speaker addresses an absent person or inanimate object

Cadence: rhythmic flow

Elegy: a mournful poem; a lament for the dead

Figurative Language: language whose intended meaning is somewhat different than the literal interpretation of the words; examples of figurative language include metaphor, simile, personification, etc.

Imagery: descriptive words or phrases that appeal to the senses; imagery often utilizes figurative language

Literary Devices: the techniques an author employs in a work; this includes alliteration, imagery, simile, metaphor, rhyme, etc.

Metaphor: a figure of speech that directly compares two unlike objects by highlighting the parts of each that are alike, related, or similar; an extended metaphor is a metaphor that continues over multiple sentences, or throughout an entire work.
>Example: In Amy Lowell's "The Pleiades," when musing about what stars look like, the speaker says they might be the toys of a little boy:
>>"Perhaps his **jackstones** which today,
>>He has forgot to put away."

Unlike a simile, the comparison is made directly, without the use of helping words ("as" or "like"). Obviously there are not really jackstones stuck in the sky, but by referring to the stars as a boy's toy "jackstones," the object is to draw out the similarities in how stars look scattered across the night sky, and how jackstones look when left scattered by a child on the ground.

Motif: a theme, idea, or image that recurs throughout a work; an element of a work (imagery, language, structure, etc.) that has symbolic significance and occurs throughout. Seemingly unrelated parts of a work can be connected by a motif through the use of common imagery, theme, or stylistic devices.

Onomatopoeia: a word that imitates the sound it is describing
>Example: "When I nodded, nearly napping, suddenly there came a **tapping**" (From Edgar Allan Poe's "The Raven")

The word "tapping" imitates the sound you would hear should someone or something tap on a door.

Personification: giving human qualities, characteristics, or emotions to inanimate objects or ideas.
>Example: In "Time, You Old Gypsy Man," time is personified as an old man, always moving on, never stopping; "the **watchful** night-wind" in Longfellow's "Paul Revere's Ride" (wind doesn't have the ability to be "watchful," but this conveys that the wind seems to be everywhere, and that there is a sense of anticipation in the air.

Refrain: a line or phrase that is repeated at intervals in a poem, usually at the end of a stanza. The refrain can be altered slightly for effect or emphasis. When writing out the rhyme scheme, the refrain can be denoted by "R" (i.e., ABABR, where the first and third lines rhyme, the second and fourth lines rhyme, and the fifth line is the refrain).

      Example: "Sail on!" from Joaquin Miller's "Columbus" is repeated at the end of each stanza, with slight variation.

If a refrain is longer (more than one line), it may fit into the rhyme scheme of the rest of the poem, and be written out as such, and not denoted by an "R."

      Example: The refrain from "The Misty Mountains" by Tolkien

Rhyme: the repetition of identical vowel sounds in stressed syllables (i.e., *found* and *hound*). In poetry, this most often connects the end of one line with the end of another.

      Example: "By day you cannot see the **sky**,

           For it is up so very **high**." (from Amy Lowell's "The Pleiades")

This type of rhyme is called masculine rhyme (or full rhyme); there are other kinds of rhymes that are not considered "full" rhyme, but are used often in poetry:

  Half rhyme: also called near or slant rhyme, a type of partial rhyme where the vowel sounds are close but not perfect; words have matching final consonants (i.e., *most* and *lost*)

  Rhyme riche: full rhyming words with identical sounds but different spellings and meanings (homophones) (i.e., *bare* and *bear*; *hair* and *hare*)

  Pararhyme: when all the consonant sounds in two words match, but the vowel sounds do not (i.e., *simmer* and *summer*; *pet* and *pit*)

  Internal rhyme: also called medial rhyme; when two words rhyme within the same line of poetry

  Example: "Once upon a midnight **dreary**, while I pondered weak and **weary**" (from Poe's "The Raven")

Rhyme scheme: the rhyming pattern in a poem. The rhyme scheme is denoted by assigning a letter to each set of rhyming words in a stanza. If the poem has a refrain, that line can be denoted by an "R."

Example:	By day you cannot see the **sky**	A
	For it is up so very **high**.	A
	You look and look, but it's so **blue**	B
	That you can never see right **through**.	B

      Alternate rhyme: a rhyme scheme in which alternate lines rhyme

Example:	O what a joy to clamber **there**,	A
	O what a place for **play**,	B
	With the sweet, the dim, the dusty **air**,	A
	The happy hills of **hay**!	B

      Couplet: a set of two lines that rhyme, usually separated into stanzas of two lines, but not always

Example:	I think I shall never **see**
	A poem as lovely as a **tree**

A tree whose hungry mouth is **prest**

Against the sweet earth's flowing **breast**; (from Kilmer's "Trees")

Simile: a figure of speech that compares two unlike things using the words "like," "as," "if," or "than"

Examples: "While hammers fell **like** ringing bells (from Tolkien's "The Dwarves' Song")

The hammers are not actually turning into ringing bells as they fall, but the simile conveys that the *sound* of the hammers falling is comparable to the *sound* of ringing bells, without saying it explicitly.

"There is no frigate **like** a book" (from Dickinson's "There is no frigate like a book")

A book is physically nothing like a large transportation boat, but the characteristic that is being brought out by the comparison is that, like a boat, a book can transport you to another destination, only it is a transportation of the mind and imagination, instead of a physical transportation.

Speaker: the voice of the poem; could also be called the narrator. It is tempting to confuse or combine the speaker of a poem and its author, but they are not necessarily the same, and should be treated as separate entities.

Example: In "The Hayloft" by Robert Louis Stevenson, we assume that the speaker is a child, but that Robert Louis Stevenson was not a child when he wrote the poem.

Stanza: the grouping of lines in a poem, usually separated from the next stanza by a space; comparable to a paragraph in prose. Some poems have a strict structure, with uniform stanzas, while others have stanzas of varying length and structure.

Synecdoche: referring to one part of something to stand in for the whole

Example: In Tennyson's "The Lady of Shalott," when the Lady sees Lancelot, it says she sees "the helmet and the plume," which we are to understand to mean that she sees Lancelot, and not just his helmet.

Tone: how the speaker feels about a subject, the attitude a speaker has towards the subject of the poem

Longfellow's poem is great for capturing the spirit and essence of Paul Revere's ride, but is not to be considered a historical source. While it seems that the exact happenings of that night are disputed, there are certain inaccuracies in the poem that are agreed upon by historians. The poem shows Revere telling his friend to shine the lights in the belfry tower as a signal to him. From historical accounts, it appears that Revere was not dependent on the lights, but rather that the lights were for the benefit of others. Revere was not the only rider to deliver the news. There were at least two other men riding with the same purpose: William Dawes and Samuel Prescott. It is also not likely that Revere himself made it to Concord. He was detained for a time by British soldiers and had his horse taken from him while he was on his way to Concord.

The poem below, "The Midnight Ride of William Dawes," is a parody to Longfellow's "Paul Revere's Ride." It was written by Helen F. Moore, and published in the *Century Magazine* in 1896.

I am a wandering, bitter shade,
Never of me was a hero made;
Poets have never sung my praise,
Nobody crowned my brow with bays;
And if you ask me the fatal cause,
I answer only, "My name was Dawes."

'Tis all very well for the children to hear
Of the midnight ride of Paul Revere;
But why should my name be quite forgot,
Who rode as boldly and well, God wot?
Why should I ask? The reason is clear—
My name was Dawes and his Revere.

When the lights from the old North Church
    flashed out,
Paul Revere was waiting about,
But I was already on my way.
The shadows of night fell cold and gray
As I rode, with never a break or a pause;
But what was the use, when my name was Dawes!

History rings with his silvery name;
Closed to me are the portals of fame.
Had he been Dawes and I Revere,
No one had heard of him, I fear.
No one has heard of me because
He was Revere and I was Dawes.